PEACE BETWEEN THE SHEETS
SEXUAL RELATIONSHIPS THAT HEAL

Dear Chris —
You are a beautiful man!
Wishing you the joy
of a healing relationship
(and soon) —
"Liz Estrada"
9/3/02

PEACE BETWEEN THE SHEETS
SEXUAL RELATIONSHIPS THAT HEAL

Liz Estrata

This book is dedicated to Gary B. Wilson, whose courage, knowledge and open heart finally brought it to life.

PEACE BETWEEN THE SHEETS
SEXUAL RELATIONSHIPS THAT HEAL

TABLE OF CONTENTS

Preface

This book is about fresh hope for relationships. It is guaranteed to restore your optimism if you're tired of watching your relationships deteriorate despite powerful initial attraction, or if you've been feeling a growing despondency about the prospect of an intimate relationship. In fact, whether you're contemplating your first intimate relationship or are a veteran of the sexual revolution who has explored passion freely, you are likely to find its suggestions inspiring...eventually.

Peace Between the Sheets has been a long time in the making. One fragment of it arrived years before I ever thought of writing a book. On a visit to my boyfriend's college fraternity my curiosity led me to pick up a *Playboy* magazine. After duly examining Miss April, I happened upon the results of a reader survey that had asked, "What makes for the best sex?" The answer that received the greatest percentage of votes was, "being deeply in love with your partner."

Decades later, I can finally explain why those readers were correct. The benefits to us of caring selflessly about another person are profound. Not only do such feelings change our outlook on life for the better, they also have physiological effects. They reduce stress, heal us and even rejuvenate us. Sexual intimacy that can do all this is truly great sex. And to experience it continuously all we have to do is stay in love.

Indeed, if logic ruled we would stay in love. The problem is that—for the present—biology rules. That is, when sex enters our relationship, our so-called primitive brain, or limbic system, takes over, and its agenda has nothing to do with staying in love or even personal well-being. Its job is strictly to multiply the species as frequently as possible. So, from its perspective, cockroaches are a more successful species than humans, simply because there are more of them. It often causes us to make choices without thinking, and when allowed free rein, it is so powerful that it dictates our behavior even when we don't want to produce children.

This impulsive, primitive brain is the source of our passion reflex. It manipulates us to stop thinking clearly whenever we become sexually aroused by stimulating the pleasure/reward center of our brains. This is the center associated with all addictions, and, even if we do not become sex addicts according to a clinical definition, we do begin to view others through a veil of pleasure/reward hunger.

This craving is far from innocuous. It can make us sexually demanding, but often it takes other forms that bear no obvious relation to our sex lives. It may, for example, cause us to crave constant emotional reassurance, more time for ourselves, "comfort" food or drink, material security or a baby. All this happens unconsciously and innocently, but, because of it, sexual intimacy often adds an artificial *urgency* to our inclinations. Sadly, this inflated sense of lack also distorts our perception of others because, when we project it onto them, we tend to judge their motives harshly regardless of their true intentions. It's easy to see how the fallout from this addictive response to sexual activity engenders distrust between the sexes. No wonder we see so much painful emotional or physical distance in our relationships.

Intimate union heals. Addictive craving, however, is like a virus of separation. It erodes relationships. And when they end, or become empty shells of mutual defensiveness, the healing stops. You may already see that to get around this problem we have to wrest control of our love lives from our primitive brain. We can do this by consciously switching the focus of our relationships from fertilization behavior to mutual nurturing—that is, from *get* to *give*. Yet good intentions alone won't put us in the driver's seat. We also have to learn to make love another way—a way that fulfills us without leaving us vulnerable to biology's wiles.

The solution I propose is straightforward and logical once you comprehend the need for it. It retains a potent attraction between lovers and the goal of reuniting them in a completely satisfying way, but it achieves its goal differently...by circumventing our primitive passion reflex. Heating up to explode in orgasm is no longer the goal.

This solution is ancient. Esoteric traditions across the globe furnish clues about it. Yet for me mere clues were not enough. Indeed, I learned about the practical aspects of this approach the long way because I kept trying to mix passion with giving. Eventually I couldn't miss the fact that even these two well-intentioned pursuits were like oil and water. They always eventually led to defensiveness and separation on the part of both my partner and me. In hopes that you can avoid such detours, this book recommends consistency, and includes simple, non-esoteric instructions.

The rewards of shifting the focus of your intimate relationship away from passion may surprise you. An easy harmony and warm companionship is likely to flower rapidly. You may find you laugh more than in any past relationship. Best of all, those *Playboy* readers were right; it's thrilling to be in the arms of someone you adore when you know unequivocally that they feel the same way about you. There's nothing boring about it, even without hot sex.

Encounter after encounter, you continue to experience every touch as delicious—instead of an unsettling cycle of magnetic attraction followed by repulsion. Indeed, you're always surprisingly enthusiastic about snuggling because you never kill your desire. Intercourse offers a comforting sense of fulfillment—but does not become the entire point of your intimacy. And you continue to look attractive to each other because, with no subconscious uneasiness, each of you associates the other only with the benefits of union.

With your attention on caring for each other, you also experience a high level of trust. This creates the safety to share your feelings and release old defenses. And truly profound experiences of union can happen:

> **Suddenly we both seemed to be floating in an unbounded space filled with warmth and light. The boundaries between our bodies dissolved and, along with them, the distinctions between man and woman. We were one. The experience became timeless, and we seemed to remain like this forever.**

> **There was no need to have an orgasm. There was no need to "make love." There was nothing to do, nothing to achieve. We were in ecstasy.**
>
> *Sacred Sexuality*[1]

Peace Between the Sheets has two parts. The first explores in greater depth why we would be wise to leave our current sexual habits behind. It is likely to confront a few cherished assumptions of most readers as it recommends avoiding masturbation as much as possible, learning to make love without conventional orgasm, healing all alienation from the opposite sex, and putting relationship harmony before all conventional agendas for intimacy.

If you are like I am, nothing will convince you of the validity of this approach as effectively as giving it a try. Therefore, the second part of the book is a series of activities for couples who wish to defy the automatic programming of their primitive brains and heal any residual uneasiness about intimacy using the selfless exchange of sexual energy. They are called, *"The Ecstatic Exchanges."*

Here's an account of a friend's recent experience with it:

More than ten months ago I agreed to try the *Exchanges*. I had my reservations. Number one, I'd never been able to sleep comfortably through the night with anyone. Number two, I wasn't thrilled about making love according to some "recipe" that sounded like *it* would tell *me* when I could have intercourse. Three, I didn't know her *that way* and it felt weird to start on a program that envisioned making love some weeks down the road. Four, I liked jerking off as much as anyone (about three or four times a week), and I knew I'd have to give up ejaculation.

I had read the material, though, and it perfectly described the roller coaster of my previous relationships. Finally I understood why I'd always pulled away to find my own "space," or gotten into pointless arguments with my lovers. I sensed this approach to sex might be the

4

answer. A few months earlier I'd broken up again with the mother of my son, with whom I'd had a painful, on-and-off-again relationship. I'd started drinking immediately after we got together the first time, fifteen years earlier.

By the time I started the *Exchanges* my life was a mess. I was in financial ruin and my drinking had increased to the point where I knew I was an alcoholic. I was spiraling downward and I didn't know how to get myself back up.

Some effects of the *Exchanges* were surprisingly rapid. After only three days I felt more comfortable and relaxed in my body. Kissing started to feel like a whole different experience—like my first kisses many years earlier. Outcome-based sex fell away. And my focus on my genitals started to shift to more of a focus on sharing.

Other changes followed. The problem of being able to sleep with someone disappeared entirely, though the first few nights were challenging. Now I love holding her when I awaken in the night before we fall back asleep.

The addiction took longer to address—in part because I tried to hide it from her while I tried to stop on my own...repeatedly...and with no success. When it came out in the open I was sure she would leave...but she didn't. Instead we became partners in addressing it. It has been more than six months since I've had any alcohol and I haven't had cravings or withdrawal symptoms. Occasionally I've had some thoughts about drinking...always following overheating my partner or myself. Previously, I used alcohol to escape from the pain of relationships. But with this approach the relationship was a source of inspiration and strength.

I haven't ejaculated at all since the relationship began ten months ago, and the desire to have orgasm isn't really present—though I'm sure could if I wanted to. There have been no ill effects from not ejaculating. I've had only one experience of genital discomfort, which occurred when my partner overheated me with classic foreplay.

The biggest difference between this relationship and my others is that we feel like teenagers, even though I'm 46 and she's two years older. We spend an hour or two kissing every day and make love frequently. The energy's been like that between us from the beginning—except for a few detours into "relationship hell," brought on by too much passion, which led to her climaxing. They've convinced me that if we were engaging in conventional sex my relationship with her would be as dismal as any of my past relationships.

I've seen big changes in other aspects of my life, too. My finances are sorting themselves out, and my professional life is expanding in directions I'd always wanted it to—but was unable to take it before. The opportunities continue to flow to me effortlessly and work out great. I have a lot more confidence in myself. I'm calm and focused. And I'm now comfortable with being in a partnership instead of seeing myself as a separate entity that happens to be involved with someone at the same time.

I'm much more optimistic about relationships, and if I had to begin again with another partner I would do it this way. It's the only way to do it.

What can you expect from doing the *Exchanges*? That depends on a single quality: your willingness. If you are prepared to try them as written, all the other qualities you associate with healthy relationships will gradually crystallize around this one. So if you have a partner who wants to give them a try, begin. Don't wait for your partner to exhibit the attributes you are looking for, such as mutual interests, generosity, physical beauty, sobriety, communication skills, or even perfect integrity. Many of us have been feeling battered by the battle biology has pitched between the sexes in its blind drive to multiply. By now we may even have given up on contact with the opposite sex entirely. We're all wilted plants. The *Exchanges* are sacred water—safe, selfless contact that gently opens our hearts, closes the gap between the genders, and restores us to wholeness. Once restored, we exude charisma, and move toward our most noble behavior as unconsciously as green plants seek the sun.

This book is a road map. It could not have been compiled or published without the generous help of many friends, lovers, friends of lovers, and lovers of friends. Some were brave enough to try the ideas; others enabled my life to run smoothly as I moved between Europe and the States. Still others helped by critiquing my ideas at every turn, contributing their own gems of experience and inspiration, building websites, drawing pictures, proofreading, solving graphics crises, or simply loving me even though my strange vocation made no sense to them whatsoever. I am deeply indebted to this chain of enthusiasts and guardians, which stretches from California to Bavaria with special links in Belgium, Arizona, New York, England, and Florida.

It is my sincere hope that with the help of this map you will be able to avoid mankind's unsuspected obstacles to deep union and create the intimate relationship for which your soul has yearned.

Liz Estrata, 2002

Note of Thanks

I wish to acknowledge the humorous people whose jokes about the current friction between the sexes I couldn't resist adding to this book (in a separate typeface). Your wry creativity helped me see the gender gap more clearly, and the laughter you provoked helped heal it.

PART I

There is a principle which is a bar against all information,
which is proof against all arguments
and which cannot fail to keep a man in everlasting ignorance.
That principle is contempt prior to investigation.

Herbert Spencer
19th Century British Philosopher

Chapter 1
Why Do We Fall Out of Love?

Dialogue Between the Sexes

She: Have you ever begun a relationship with someone you were quite attracted to—and yet very soon you found yourself wondering, "eeeeek! Who IS this creature?"

He: Definitely. She usually gives me a long list of things that are wrong with me—and that's only a few weeks after she said I was the perfect man.

She: That makes me think of that old Richard Prior album where he said, "I don't mind women leaving me…but they always have to tell you *why.*"

He: Exactly. I always think I'm doing OK…until I get to #445 of her perfect man list, and then I put the jelly on the *second* shelf of the fridge…and suddenly our relationship is a minefield. I just want to give up, get away…go have some beers.

She: And then there's the woman's side of it. When I get crazy like that it's because I'm desperately trying to make the point that my partner has pulled away and something is horribly wrong.

He: It happens even if I stick around.

She: At some level you've left. You've become self-absorbed, insensitive. When it happens to me it seems like my lover just got what he wanted and now he doesn't care anymore. After I've opened myself to someone so deeply, a lack of gratitude or consideration enrages me. I can't help sprouting live snakes for hair….

He: Well, how am I supposed to snuggle up to Medusa…?

She: Good point.

Ever fallen in love with someone who loved you back? What an experience! Suddenly the world begins to make sense. With higher voltage you flow with inspired ideas. Life takes on a rosy glow, and the wings and halo of your loved one are clearly visible. Yet if things take their normal course, you will soon look back on this brief interval of heightened awareness as the honeymoon period, and regard it as a sort of...deception.

It's not a deception. Something quite real is going on. A complete circuit of energy is flowing between your hearts, and it is actually making you more energetic, expanding your perception, and profoundly improving your body chemistry. Indeed, when humanity learns to follow this spiraling energy upward all the way we will tap something truly profound. According to various sacred sexuality traditions across the globe this flowing circuit between lovers is nothing less than a path to enlightenment.

For now, however, most of us never make it anywhere near the penthouse. Instead we get off somewhere around the third floor and swiftly begin that familiar downward spiral into the mundane...too often followed by a nosedive. This happens because the physical part of us is operating on biological autopilot and we've assumed its will is our will.

The DNA Conspiracy

Some years back, Richard Dawkins wrote a book called, *The Selfish Gene*[2]. In it he explained that all earthly life forms could be viewed as nothing more than vehicles for chains of DNA competing to replicate. DNA's goal is quantity, not quality. It cares nothing for your happiness, your health, the harmony in your relationship, or your spiritual growth. It just wants you to fertilize eggs and reproduce more greedy little strands of genes.

Despite our egocentric thinking, DNA does not even select for the "fittest." It blindly selects for hosts with careless or shortsighted procreation habits. Societies with such habits routinely procreate themselves into over-crowding, environmental destruction, epidemics and extreme poverty. Though we often deny it, blind replication behavior is not in our best interests on any level. Not only does it lead to careless pregnancies, it also—without our realizing it—promotes uneasiness between the sexes.

For example, this DNA conspiracy creates distrust. To generalize for a moment—men, when blindly following biology's commands, search to engage in as much fertilization behavior as possible until duty calls them to their next pollination opportunity. The number of people who have been sexually abused or emotionally scarred because of this "fertilization madness" is staggering—and appears to be rising. Such shortsighted behavior accounts for widespread fear of men.

Yet women under biology's spell are equally powerfully programmed to ignore the welfare of others. They are encoded to produce babies— regardless of their circumstances—and have them supported, often at the expense of men or society. Such behavior is obviously a major cause of distrust between the sexes, too. Two friends come to mind who are both bankrupt because their lovers got pregnant and insisted on having children against the men's wills—even though the relationships were not stable, there was severe economic hardship, and the women were not "right to lifers." It's no wonder these men grew wary of relationships with women.

Such aggressive behaviors are fundamentally innocent because the perpetrators are under biological hypnosis. For example, male biology zombies—whatever their ages—find themselves helplessly attracted to women who look like they could replicate a lot of DNA, i.e., *young* women. This occurs even if they don't consciously wish to be fathers and would genuinely find the companionship of a peer more comforting. We judge men to be emotionally shallow while biology bewitches them, but women who think nothing of selecting mates according to an ideal-father list are no less shallow. The point is that biological selfishness is so powerful it can subvert free will. Biology also mandates that we make love in a way that ultimately shifts our sense of well-being for the worse.

The Hidden Hangover

We've assumed that because sex is necessary for procreation, we're pretty much at biology's mercy when it comes to how to "do it." Yet constant replication efforts not only pit the sexes against each other, they also exhaust us. Many sacred sex texts imply that the sole problem is the male "seed" expended in fertilization behavior, but any decrease in nurturing between partners is also a problem. Soon-to-be fathers will attest that they receive much less affection once their mates' attention shifts to tiny socks and shoes.

More importantly, there is a hidden cost to conventional orgasm and it affects both sexes. You can think of it as blast of body chemicals that leaves you with a sense of lack. It shifts your perception of the world for the worse as soon as the more ephemeral initial high wears off. As one tantra expert put it, orgasm temporarily kills your inner Buddha.[3] As a result, at some point afterward, you feel like something is not right—and the trouble begins.

> When sex evaporated from my marriage bed, I thought that what had been missing was passion. In fact I *prayed* for the return of what I called "passion" in my life. It surfaced in the form of a red haired Scorpio who looked *good* in hot pants. At some point during the roller coaster ride that followed, I stumbled upon a dictionary definition of passion. *"Any intense emotion"*, it said, such as *"the sufferings of Jesus upon the cross."* Sure enough I'd found passion, all right. Brief as it was, our relationship made crucifixion look kind of appealing. I now realize that what I really want is *love...* not *suffering.*
>
> *Christopher*

Basically, we are using each other as biology intends and it triggers a severe energetic hangover, or sense of lost power. This is an unsettling experience that leaves both partners feeling drained at a subconscious level. In the days following conventional sex we begin to demand more and give less, or we want more distance and less union.

The hangover can take more than two weeks to heal—and it gets radically worse before it is over. This is why sexually active relationships so often feel like seesaw rides—various unsynchronized sine waves are oscillating through them, creating seemingly random highs and lows. I suspect this hangover accounts for Orthodox Judaism's recommended two-week abstinence from intercourse each month. It gave partners a chance to get back on an even keel.

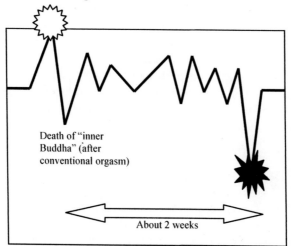

As we join in ecstasy, we see the "divine" in our loved one.

Death of "inner Buddha" (after conventional orgasm)

About 2 weeks

As our hangover kicks in, we see nothing but flaws— or reason for panic.

Conventional Orgasm and Hangover

When partners hit low points in the cycle, each usually projects his or her stress onto the other. Whereas both looked divine while they felt whole enough to allow the "urge to merge" to flow, the reverse happens once they feel uneasy. Typically, he begins to look (to her) impossibly self-centered, insensitive and selfish, while she looks (to him) frighteningly needy, dissatisfied and demanding.

To be sure, these roles are not gender specific and the disharmony may take many other forms. When both pull away immediately, we call that a "one night stand." And when both get needy we call that "co-dependence."

Have a Laugh at the Gender Gap...
If a man says something in the middle of the forest, and there is no woman around to hear him...is he still *wrong?*

Don't think you can change a man...unless he's in diapers.

The Internet

Usually, however, one lover pulls away while the other desperately seeks to prevent the impending separation by manipulating, over-controlling or provoking guilty feelings. Each looks frightening to the other, which breaks the circuit of love that was flowing between them. They are no longer nourishing each other because their hearts have closed in defensiveness. Usually one goes extremely "yin," creating an unhealthy suction in the relationship, while the other goes extremely "yang" and pushes the other away.

"I'll die without you!" *or* "Come back—or you're a creep."

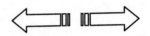

"I'm being devoured! I MUST get away" *or* "I'll drive *you* away."

Fear Breaks the Circuit between Lovers

During this hangover period we have a powerful sense that something isn't right. And it isn't. Unfortunately the whole planet is suffering from this syndrome, which I call the *separation virus.* So we keep trying to convince each other our distress is "just life," or can be fixed by tackling some aspect of ourselves, or can be avoided by being more selective next time. As the problem keeps recurring, our "must have" lists for future mates gets longer and longer.

It's easy to fool ourselves that sex has nothing to do with our distress because the symptoms of this skewed perception usually don't show up first as sexual problems. Instead they show up as "obvious personality flaws" in our lover or ourselves—like addiction, nagging, insensitivity, irresponsible spending, paranoia, stinginess and compelling attractions to third parties. And so we attack the symptoms—instead of the cause.

Except for Mom and Dad in *The Brady Bunch*, I know of no couples who've escaped the effects of this fallout for more than the first six months of a committed relationship. Even the happiest looking marriages reveal startling gaps behind the scenes. (See Chapter 6) It's obvious there is something more than random bad luck going on—or at least half of all couples would be blissfully content and making love a lot. They aren't.

Our DNA damages our peace of mind by urging us to meet its goals. Unless we learn to override its commands, we will continue to see our relationships mutate into uncomfortable truces. In short, as long as we travel through matter in gender costumes there will be sexual desire. But it's dangerous to assume biology's use of it is benign.

Tricks Biology Plays

Scientists (and you have to suspect that it gets lonely in the lab with experiments like this one...) have shown that if you sexually exhaust a male rat with one female his body chemistry will reflect his exhaustion. However, if he's placed with a new female, his body chemistry of fatigue will swiftly disappear and he will gallantly fulfill his fertilization duties without hesitation. This is known as, "The Coolidge Effect." [Fiorino, D.F. et al., "Dynamic Changes in Nucleus Accumbens Dopamine Efflux During the Coolidge Effect in Male Rats" *(1997) Journal of Neuroscience*, June, 17:12., 4849-55]

Does the "The Coolidge Effect" show up in human behavior, too? Well...I recall a conversation I once had with a man who'd grown up in sensual Los Angeles. "I quit counting at 350 lovers," he confessed, "and I guess there must be something terribly wrong with me because I always lost interest in them sexually so quickly. Some of those women are really beautiful, too." When I met him, his third wife had just left him for a Frenchman and he was discouraged.

[continued...]

Gandhi himself may have suffered from a touch of "Coolidge-itis." It is rumored that while he was fasting to protest British colonialism he slept between two virgins to invigorate himself. He had long since given up sex with his wife, of course, in favor of celibate spiritual practice. History has not recorded whether Mrs. Gandhi conducted a similar experiment to raise her spirits in the absence of her husband's attentions.

And then there's the tale of how the "Coolidge Effect" got its name. Many years ago, President Coolidge and his wife were touring a farm. While the President was elsewhere, the farmer pointed out to Mrs. Coolidge a rooster that "could copulate with hens all day long, day after day." Mrs. Coolidge said, "tell that to Mr. Coolidge." The farmer did. The President thought for a moment and then inquired, "with the same hen?" "No, Sir" replied the farmer. "Tell that to Mrs. Coolidge," said the President.

Humanity is on the verge of recognizing the subconscious costs of its primitive sexual behavior. Popular relationship therapist, John Gray (*Men are from Mars, Women are from Venus*), teaches that men are like rubber bands, and that their pattern of horniness and release followed by periods of emotional alienation from their partners is harmless. I admire his clear articulation of the problem: "Men, you *must* get away from women after periods of intimacy, or they will *drain* you. Women, when that happens, go whine to other women until your man is prepared to *sacrifice* again for loving contact with you." As we will see, the partners have actually created a feeling of lack themselves, and their sense of sacrifice, or dissatisfaction, is a projection of their uneasiness.

If you remember *The Celestine Prophecy*, you'll recall that the protagonist is forbidden to form a relationship with a woman because their relationship would "pull them from the paths of their individual evolution and lead to a hopeless power struggle." Both these authors—without realizing it—are talking about the hangover problem that accompanies conventional intimate relationships. Gray highlights the need to recover (and perhaps underestimates the destructiveness of men's belief that they need to sacrifice to have loving contact). Redfield advocates avoidance so his main character doesn't risk losing his power—at least "until people learn how to empower themselves."

Women authors are addressing the same distress. In addition to producing a host of "negotiating for the relationship you want" books, women are beginning to counsel avoidance as well. *Sensual Celibacy* by Donna Marie Williams proposes avoiding sex to recharge your spirit and figure out what *you* like in bed, and *Solitaire: The Intimate Lives of Single Women* by Marian Botsford Fraser salutes single life. We do need to learn to empower ourselves, but despite the convincing evidence that relationships drain us, avoidance—except as a regrouping measure—is not the most effective path to personal power.

Relationships that Heal

Relationships can be the solution instead of the problem. You can learn to prevent any artificial alienation between lovers and heal the damage inflicted by primitive-brain programming. In the process a reliable path to harmonious, nurturing union emerges.

The first step is to lay down a new subconscious pattern of enjoyable intimacy without the energy crash and hangover. Instead of going for the tension-and-release orgasm, you choose a new approach to sex—one that doesn't deplete you or tarnish your perception of each other. All of those delightful highs you have when you first fall in love continue. This means every affectionate touch or kiss feels as good as the first. And your libido stays "on" so you both always welcome the opportunity to nurture each other with affectionate exchanges.

Imagine knowing that your partner always enjoys making love with you, but at the same time feels so well cared for that he or she never demands any type of sexual performance (or resents not having it). This easy harmony is entirely possible and relatively simple to attain. We just have to tiptoe past the biological urge.

As you learn to maintain a lighthearted, pleasurable feeling in your relationship, you no longer view the absence of the tension-and-release orgasm—with its emphasis on quantity and related performance woes—as a sacrifice. Indeed if you and a lover employ the suggestions in this book, the burning desire for this type of orgasm passes surprisingly quickly because your body chemistry shifts. (Chapter 3) As you learn to open your hearts completely, truly remarkable states of ecstasy, which far exceed what most of us have been settling for, are also possible.

For example, here are descriptions of lovemaking experiences from *Sexual Energy Ecstasy*[4]:

> **The usual sense of having separate identities begins to dissolve. Eventually your sense of oneness becomes total. The two of you (at the life energy level) have literally become one. Thrilling oceanic wave-like feelings that are like orgasm yet different course through your bodies over and over and over again.**

> **You feel startlingly alive and clearheaded. You feel that the two of you are one. An aura of peace and benign energy is felt. The best word to describe the feeling is probably sacred. You may feel that you are on truly holy ground.**

Here are some from *Healing Love Through the Tao:*[5]

> **The valley orgasm** *[as distinct from the conventional, "peak" orgasm]* **occurs spontaneously in the deep state of relaxation, and it is a very powerful experience which I feel in every cell, every particle of my being as an exquisite, ecstatic melting. The feeling of connection with my partner is profound. My whole being is shared with his, and his with mine, as one flow that knows no boundaries....I am always in awe of the tremendous power residing in male and female. We are all closer to being gods and goddesses than we think....There is**

a sense of all the time in the world, of being in eternity, and of having more and more energy available.

And, from *Taoist Secrets of Love*[6]*:*

There have been times in the middle of lovemaking that we've both just cried, it is so powerful. That quality of tenderness, that connection. So it's definitely more than physical....*[Receiving a partner's energy is]* like fanning the fire inside yourself and then allowing yourself to melt into it....I feel fed, it's like a food...I become more balanced.

In short, you don't have to avoid the opposite sex to escape the sexual hangover syndrome. You can, in fact, strengthen each other by making love differently. When you move consistently in this direction you build your immunity to the separation virus. Your fear of closer union dissolves. Many discover that familiar sexual dysfunctions that often separate lovers (such as premature ejaculation, sexual unresponsiveness, urinary tract infection, and impotence), simply melt away in the warmth of a relationship dedicated to mutual healing.

I sometimes refer to this new goal of hangover-free, healing sex as MELTING. This term is based on an acronym for "Mutual Ecstatic Loving Transcendence." But it describes very well the feeling you have as the subconscious fear between you dissolves—leaving you with the heartfelt desire to melt into each other.

One step beyond this desire for deep union lies an ancient mystery surrounding sex. We often think of sex as mere "food" or release. Yet, when lovers use it to nurture each other, rather than serve themselves, it sets up a synergy that enhances both partners' lives in ways that appear to be totally unrelated to the act of sex. A restored sense of wholeness boosts your ability to attain your goals. It increases your energy level, centers you, helps you think more clearly, heals addictions, lets you create prosperity, and even enhances spiritual perception.

> Never be afraid to try something new. Remember, amateurs
> built the ark. Professionals built the Titanic.   *The Internet*

How I Got Hooked on Avoiding Conventional Orgasm

Of course, even with good intentions, it's not so easy to leave our current sexual habits behind. It has taken me over ten years to discover a set of stepping stones to a new approach—and I've had a lot of help. At last I can assure you that not only can it be done, the process is surprisingly enjoyable. With sufficient motivation, and clear directions (the second half of the book), you won't have to stumble around as I did.

Here's an account of one of my early attempts to crack the code: I met Alex in a workshop at a spiritual community in Scotland. He was a psychologist who was taking a break from his practice to travel from Canada around the world. After the seminar we traveled to my home on the continent together, and, following much discussion, decided to try a non-orgasmic approach to sex. I had a book, written by a man, with lots of tips on how men could gain mastery over the urge to ejaculate. It recommended tightening the muscles around the prostate gland, clenching the teeth, counting breaths and various other forceful techniques—all of which I later learned are not nearly as effective as a more relaxed, very gradual approach to sexual intimacy itself.

In any event, Alex insisted that he did not *need* any instructions. When we made love, however, it was "business as usual." That is, he ejaculated. And for the next several days exactly the same thing happened despite his genuine intention to avoid coming. I kept suggesting he study the manual but he was growing increasingly irascible. When I pointed out that, according to the book, his short temper might be due to frequent orgasm itself, he blew.

"You're crazy to suggest ejaculation has a negative effect on men, Liz. I'm a psychologist. If that were the case, I'd *know* about it. If you keep talking like this, you're going to be in a nuthouse...explaining this to your *shrink!*" I could see further argument would just make things worse. I remember thinking how nice it would be if he just got on the next train, but I managed a stony silence. Finally he exploded, "I can see you're not going to listen to a word I say until I read that book!"

"That's right, Alex," I said. "Okay, what do I have to read?" I showed him the four or five pages that explained the techniques mentioned above. He flipped through the directions and announced, "Let's go try it." At that point I was ready to give up the whole idea. This chivalrous invitation did not resemble any of *my* pictures about a sacred sexuality encounter. Yet I figured another attempt couldn't be any worse than what I'd already been through with him.

We made love according to the instructions. He clenched and counted and completed the encounter without coming. And then he amazed me with, "I don't believe it. I don't feel unsatisfied. I don't have blue balls. *Thank you for teaching me this!*" As astonishing as his newfound enthusiasm was, an even greater surprise followed. Over the next 24 hours he was a different man. His anger evaporated and his heart opened. Whereas before he'd assured me that he didn't need a partner because he was on a "spiritual path," now he opened up and talked about how much he'd always wanted a mate and was confused by his inability to stay in relationship.

The biggest shift of all was that he saw me completely differently. No longer did he recommend institutionalization. Instead he told me, "Liz, you are so spiritual and so generous. God must be really proud of you for sticking to this despite so much resistance." I transformed, too. It felt like my heart cracked open with gratitude and I could clearly see his angelic qualities. I remember thinking, "Thank you for showing me this man's true beauty."

I vowed that I'd just had my last pointless meltdown with a lover. I could smell the potential for mutual adoration and satisfying intimacy in this new approach and I was more determined than ever to master this other use of sex. As it turned out I had more senseless meltdowns still in my future because some of the vital clues for how one eludes biology (and habit) were missing from the sex manuals I began to devour. Yet at last I was fully motivated.

If you, too, are convinced that you want to learn to make love without conventional orgasm, and you have a partner, you may wish to skip to the second part of this book, "*The Ecstatic Exchanges*." The *Exchanges* comprise a method for evading biology's clutches, with a suggested program and nightly activities for couples to do together.

If you don't have a partner, or the prospect of avoiding orgasm still makes you swallow hard, read on. The next chapter recaps some of the most unsettling insights that came my way as I began to learn how the separation virus damages intimate relationships.

Chapter 2
Uncomfortable Clues

When I first learned there was a more inspired way to use sex, I imagined it was an optional enhancement for regular lovemaking…sort of like cinnamon on a cappuccino.   It turns out, however, that the unmistakable benefits of this approach (which we'll examine more closely in the next chapter) are only half the story. The other half is that our current sexual habits are actively creating chaos in our relationships. So it's ironic that, at least for the moment, humanity is more pro-orgasm than ever.

Orgasm: a *Problem* for Women?

Most women are certain that today's focus on genital orgasm is an idea whose time has come.   After all, for millennia the heavy boots of patriarchy have stomped about on our sexuality. We were relegated to the role of broodmare (the counterpart, it must be noted, of the role we now often try to put men in…). Then too, we were forced to let men have their way with us with no attention to our way, and so forth. As one liberated male explained, "Women have thousands of years of missed orgasms to make up for"—a noble task at which he was diligently beavering away.

For many of us learning to climax was a breakthrough because we previously felt we were missing out on something. Yet the pursuit of genital orgasm can ensure that we miss out on far greater benefits than forced experiences of intense, addictive pleasure.

The issue of the effect of orgasm on women is obscured by the fact that most sexual advice—even esoteric—assumes orgasm is no problem for women because we don't ejaculate semen. For years I fell for this cheerful assumption. Around 1994, however, events conspired to bring certain unwelcome truths to my attention, and, as a result, I no longer make orgasm my goal—with or without a partner.

At that time, my girlfriend, Corinne, had a new lover. He'd grown up in a culture where artificial birth control virtually didn't exist, so in order to make love as a teen he'd learned to avoid ejaculation. He regarded it as perfectly natural to explore a non-ejaculatory approach to sex with her. She was thrilled. Their lovemaking was sensational, cosmic, lengthy (the phone was once off the hook for four days while I dialed in vain...), and her capacity for multiple orgasm as boundless as ever.

But cracks were appearing. A few weeks into her romance she (finally) called and asked hesitantly, "Do you think there's any chance genital orgasm is a problem for us, too...?" I was listening very carefully. During the preceding months I'd also finally found a lover who controlled himself easily but who obviously enjoyed that I came so effortlessly. Yet we certainly weren't tapping the mystical bliss and union the sacred sex books I'd read talked about. Instead I was noticing an ugly emotional friction flickering between us.

From then on Corinne and I compared notes like scientists in a laboratory. Regardless of other variables affecting either couple, within a week or two after orgasmic encounters (no matter who came), trouble would erupt between them. Corinne tended to become weepy, oversensitive, ineffective and discouraged. I tended toward a razor tongue, impatience, pessimism and analyzing the *obviously* irreconcilable differences between my lover and me. Mood swings, which we had always before knowingly blamed on the fallout from our partners' post-ejaculation blues (as discussed in the sacred sex texts), haunted us both. Why was this happening?

24

Half the Picture

In search of an explanation for what we were experiencing, I reflected on what I'd learned about men's sexual hangovers. Look how a man's first act of intercourse with a young woman changed his perception:

> *[Before sex]* **I wanted to cry, my heart hurt, because she was so beautiful and I wanted her so much.**

> *[Afterward]* **I was a little disappointed** *[when I saw her body]*, **and her beauty no longer set me on fire as it had done when I first saw it in a haze of passion.**[7]

With the insights gleaned from sacred sex texts I began to suspect that his haze was actually a *post*-passion phenomenon that shifted his perception for the *worse*. Remember Billy Crystal in *"When Harry Met Sally?"* He said that 30 seconds after making love he wanted to get out of bed and leave. Indeed, a common male reaction to ejaculation is something like, "Well, that's obviously as good as it gets. I've achieved the goal now....I need a rest and don't feel very sexy anymore, so leave me alone." Over time this harmless need for space can bloom into antipathy—especially if he is pressed to make love:

> **Eventually a man can develop feelings of indifference or hate for his sexual partner because he subconsciously realizes that when he** [has sex with her] **he loses those higher energies that could make him a truly happy man.**[8]

It was also an eye-opener to learn that the projection of this hangover had apparently made women appear threatening to the most influential sex analyst of the last century:

> **Probably no male human being is spared the fright of castration at the sight of a female genital.** [S. Freud[9]]

Or, when sex is considered sinful, could make women seem immoral:

> [After sex with a woman men] **triumphantly feel that they have done her dirt, and now she is lower, cheaper, more contemptible than she was before. [D. H.** Lawrence[10]]

I'd even happened upon more modern versions of similar unfortunate shifts in perception, such as panic or callous self-loathing.

> **No matter who the woman was, I was as good as gone the moment we made love. It was at that moment that I always touched something taboo—my mother, my pain—and I would have to fly away ... If I didn't fly away I ran them off. Either way I knew I couldn't be with them.** [11] [John Lee]

> **I don't give a f**k about the morality of it....I didn't care. Everyone's a dirty beast.** [Actor Hugh Grant, about being caught with Divine Brown in 1995]

I saw, too, that men's mysterious distress wasn't just projected onto women. A sense of *lack* often haunted them. Herb Goldberg, in *What Men Really Want*[12], wrote:

> **The defensive nature of masculinity creates in men a deeply wary and negative experience of the world, which they see as a place where there is never enough power, control, security or independence.**

Couldn't this sense of lack originate in the energy drop associated with sex? If the problem was widespread enough for Herb [just quoted] to suggest it was part of men's nature then it must be caused by something pretty universal. As I studied the situation I began to ask bigger questions. How else might such projections of discomfort show up in humanity's experience? Could this syndrome shed light on anger and heart attacks from toxic relationships men feel trapped in? Or on centuries of popular religions based on guilt (born of uneasiness following sex)? On destructive addictions by which men punish themselves or others? Above all, on the urge to have sex but avoid ongoing intimacy?

Slowly I grasped that the shift in my partners' perceptions of me, which I had often sensed, was not strictly a product of my "stuff"—or even his. It was real. But—here's the most important point in this book—it was also *involuntary* and *preventable*. That is, men couldn't possibly stop it from occurring without addressing the underlying cause. Yet there was a way to make love differently. True, convincing someone to forego conventional orgasm isn't the *easiest* sell in the world, but I knew it wasn't impossible either. After all, I was reading books, written by men, advocating it. And, as I saw for myself the benefits to my partners of avoiding orgasm, my subconscious fear of intimacy faded. Indeed, I was becoming jubilant about relationships again.

The Other Half of the Picture

Yet now Corinne and I squirmed as we asked ourselves the same hard questions. What if some sort of perception shift from conventional orgasm also adversely affected us? How might sexual hangovers manifest in women's experience? How about all around bitchiness? Making him wrong for everything? Reaching for Prozac? Avoiding sex? Feeling unable to cope? Insane jealousy? Fortune hunting? Compulsive shopping, or even kleptomania? Tears and emotional blackmail? Neurotic, needy, controlling mothers—and wounded kids?

Why...it looked like a list of complaints from the minutes of a men's support group meeting. And maybe we couldn't do much to prevent our "bottomless pit" neediness and destructive overreactions unless we, too, addressed the underlying cause of our artificial sense of deprivation. One weary veteran was right on the money:

> **Are women crazy, or do I, without knowing exactly how, somehow make them as irrational and volatile as they seem to become after we get involved? They're rarely like that until after we get "serious."**[13]

Orgasm yields a short-term glow that sometimes makes me feel closer to my partner and the whole world for a time: loving union is very nourishing. But the fallout does descend. Get out a calendar and track your orgasms (with or without a partner), as well as your most pronounced mood swings over the following two to three weeks. If you are very open-minded, you may see the connection between cause and effect for yourself. And if you are near your partner, chances are your distress will be projected onto him. Get his opinion and watch for emotional separation between you—whoever seems to cause it. When you learn to prevent this potent source of disharmony, you will find that that all the other issues you thought were causing your discord mysteriously grow more manageable.

TIP: If you don't have conventional orgasm easily, with or without a partner, don't buy into the popular wisdom that "you have a problem." You may, in fact, be ahead of the pack. Try the *Ecstatic Exchanges* recipe at the end of this book before you conclude your sexual energy is hopelessly blocked. It may just be "on strike" until you figure out a use for it that heals and deepens your relationships instead of eroding them.

One well-known sacred sex teacher insists that the vagina does not naturally strive for orgasm. It has to be taught this habit by a society that is obsessed with "getting off," and when it learns to focus on orgasm, it becomes increasingly hard, greedy and predatory. It concentrates on orgasm, not love....and any pleasure is based on temporary, emotional satisfaction. This causes the woman deep, inner unhappiness. It's irrelevant whether or not she is promiscuous—which is only a desperate search for the love she is not finding through the pursuit of orgasm. *[Barry Long, "Making Love: Sexual Love the Divine Way" audio tape, Barry Long Books, 1996]*

A few years back I came upon a clue in black and white that confirmed what Corinne and I learned the hard way. A tantra teacher in India wrote:

[If a woman does not relax into an altered state during sex] **she will have the nervous orgasm, which is short-lived and followed by dissatisfaction and exhaustion. This is often the cause of a woman's hysteria and depression**[14]

Not to mention that of her mate....So, if harmony in your relationship is a goal, our experience suggests that women should not make the same innocent error men have of believing tension-release orgasm is the point of sex. Otherwise women could be setting up this familiar scenario:

This relationship was supposed to be different. We were bonded in spirit. But within six months we had fallen into the abyss of all that was unholy between man and woman. My physical and emotional health was severely depleted. Depression was a constant companion. Our relationship was fragmented and wounded. How could I have experienced Divine Oneness and now feel such separation from my husband? How could I endure the pain of not knowing how to close the enormous gap between us? What had happened during my marriage that warranted the comment from a new friend that I was the saddest looking woman she had ever seen? Before my marriage I was a professional educator, vibrantly alive. A year into it I felt drained of all but enough life force to survive.[15]

So, if women stop striving for genital orgasm, does this mean we give up all pleasure and return to our traditional role as asexual receptors of men's passion? Certainly not. It means that the satisfaction we've been looking for lies in a mutual experience in which both partners stop using each other for physical gratification and make nurturing each other their primary focus. As we'll see in the next chapter this causes a shift in body chemistry that heightens sexual responsiveness and makes all contact surprisingly delicious.

The first time I had orgasm effortlessly during intercourse was in my thirties when I made love with a man who was a virgin. My attention was not on myself at all. I was focused entirely on making him feel safe and loved so the experience would always be a warm memory of loving intimacy. From that encounter onward I've been very orgasmic. And even though I now do my best to avoid orgasm because of the hangover, I still find that making my partner feel comfortable and adored is a sure turn-on for me. When he puts me first, too, it's heaven.

The Big Picture

Could a perfectly natural hangover really explain so much? Despite my initial resistance, I had to admit that the evidence was convincing. Just about everyone makes love or is affected by people suffering from this recurring sense of lack. The sociological and economic explanations for human behavior I'd studied began to seem incomplete. I saw that they could be addressing *symptoms* of a more fundamental force—mankind's chronic sense of deprivation (self-induced). That perennial condition could certainly account for our greed, manipulative behavior, violence, unhealthy subservience, misuse of power, fuzzy decision-making, false sense of weakness, chauvinistic behavior, and so forth. On a wide scale these tendencies cried out for historical or economic explanations, and yet perhaps they arose from a common cause.

It was as if a floodlight went on. Nothing looked the same. For one thing, if we were doing this to ourselves as a species, maybe we could change it. True, biology had encoded us for certain behavior, but apparently it was possible to install new software. What if we learned to make love without allowing our primitive brains to trigger this haunting sense of deprivation? Imagine the enormous potential of learning to maintain an inner state of abundance and vitality instead. Generosity, the flexibility to try new approaches, and a balanced perspective about how to employ resources would become as natural as breathing. If practiced widely, this shift would reflect back a fundamentally different society. Maybe the metaphysicians were right that we could create a very different reality. My enthusiasm for this new approach increased again.

30

Yet that old biological itch was a formidable foe. Thwarted by the baffling alienation between the sexes, many of us had taken matters into our own hands. As you might expect, I was gleaning some unwelcome insights about masturbation, too, but let's start that part of the story—as I did—from a modern, mainstream vantage point.

If it weren't for pickpockets, I'd have no sex life at all.

Rodney Dangerfield

Having sex is like playing bridge. If you don't have a good partner, you'd better have a good hand.   *The Internet*

Q: How did Pinocchio discover he was made of wood?
A: His hand caught fire.   *The Internet*

Orgasm is Orgasm

If you haven't checked out the magazines in the grocery line for a while you might have missed the fact that masturbation is currently touted as a panacea—especially for women, but also for couples. Even Catholics are at last abandoning the nonsensical notion that masturbation is sinful, so good ole do-it-yourself sex appears to be the obvious solution…for everyone…for lots of things.

For example, it's a ready option when your post-orgasmic perception hangover makes your current partner sexually uninteresting. It also lets you find out how to have the most explosive orgasm possible, demonstrate for your lover—and provide for yourself when your lover lets you down. For many of us it's a sure fire tranquilizer. And, of course, it's a way to relieve sexual frustration in between lovers.

Unfortunately all these rationalizations can lead you away from the goal of blissful harmony with another. The more you drain yourself, the worse your partner will look. The more you chase explosive genital gratification, the more separation will unexpectedly erupt between you. And—perhaps most surprisingly of all—the more you masturbate, the more you decrease your power to attract a balanced partner.

In short, whether we're pushed off a bridge or choose to jump, we still hit the water with a smack. So regular masturbation is not the ideal means of managing our sexual energy. This, of course, does not imply that you should be afraid to touch your genitals, find out where things are, or be ashamed of what they are capable of doing. Yet continuing to research and practice what trips your trigger is of no benefit whatsoever if you wish to use sex to heal. You will have to move your prime focus from your genitals to your heart, so why not get started?

The ultimate solution for sexual frustration is regular, nourishing exchange with a lover, and, if you are without a partner, there are suggestions for the interim later in this chapter. Meanwhile, I want to touch on some aspects of masturbation that the grocery store magazines forget to mention.

As Chapter 4 will explain, masturbation, like any genital orgasm, releases brain chemicals that promote addiction. So despite the initial relief a quick orgasm furnishes, it's junk food that leaves you feeling deprived at another level. You can swiftly become hooked on physical stimulation—and conclude that "getting off," not union, is the point of having genitals.

The hangover can leave you with a sense that something vital is lacking or you are helpless to restore your sense of well-being. It may take a familiar form, such as discouragement, feeling painfully different from others, obstinacy, distrust, cynicism, baffling exhaustion, insomnia, and so forth—and you will not connect these feelings with frequent orgasm. Indeed, you may be certain that masturbation has had no ill effects on you. Yet, until you're clear of any addiction, you can't accurately judge its effects.

Two of my friends who were addicted to masturbation ended up on Prozac for "inexplicable" depression. Such uneasiness also furnishes fertile ground for other addictions, like pot and alcohol. So, as I cheerfully say to people, "never feel bad about masturbating....It will make you feel bad enough." And it will do so whether or not you feel guilty about it. Guilt is just one version of the post-orgasm hangover. It may well take another form—like a feeling you're being treated unfairly. Combine knowledge about this hangover with a new optimism about intimate relationships and you will find it relatively easy to abandon any further attempts at self-sufficiency and move purposefully toward union.

Even as a tranquilizer masturbation has some hidden costs. The hangover from orgasm can impair judgment, causing a tendency to evade responsibility or jump nervously from one activity to the next in a hyperactive, but unproductive, manner. It can also promote, irritability or a tendency to over-control. For example, I've noticed that frequent "self pleasuring" tends to make some of my women friends especially brittle, particularly judgmental of men—and subject to intense mood swings. Behaviors like these alienate others more effectively than hairy palms. They are like ugly disguises that give us (and others) a very convincing, but false, impression of who we really are.

Masturbation also encourages fantasizing, and a compelling fantasy routine can entice you to remain in your own private world of self-gratification. Or, even when you connect with someone, you may find yourself prisoner of your mental movie theater and not fully present with your lover. While fantasy generally plays a big role in conventional sexual therapy you won't need it at all with this approach. Orgasm is no longer the goal, and avoiding it *will* increase your libido.

> **You asked why I've stopped masturbating. It's because I feel stronger and happier from day to day. I wouldn't believe it if I didn't experience it. There's also a laughing feeling in the stomach and throat all the time. Wonderful! My desire for social activities of any kind is much greater than one week or so after masturbating. I long for interaction with women, and it's just fine to exchange smiles here and there, or talk a little bit, etc.**
>
> **I remember that last year, before I tried to stop (or cut back...), I was constantly depressed. I did it nearly every other day and**
> *[continued...]*

33

> sometimes 3 or 4 times a day. It's rather hard to stop this addiction but THERE'S MUCH TO BE GAINED. In general: an awareness of the oneness of all.
>
> Masturbation is a very powerful 'instrument' to keep up the illusion of separation. This is the ultimate (spiritual) consequence of this 'practice.'   *Karl*

Increasing Sexual Magnetism

As the saying goes, "like attracts like." So if you want to attract a relationship with the potential for balanced exchange, reach out and touch someone *else*. When you stop masturbating your sexual magnetism increases. Some of the most seductive men on the planet hale from the West Indies. They take pride in using their sex appeal to draw women to them. They are successful in part because masturbation is not a big part of their culture. As a Jamaican friend once crooned when I asked about masturbation in Jamaica, "Nooooooo…if you can't get a woman, dar is someting wrong wit you, mon." So, whether you're male or female, don't be afraid to charge up your battery. It will increase your charisma. You'll make more of an effort to connect with others, and the more you do, the better you'll feel.

> **Feel the Power**
> As we were falling asleep after making love, I noticed that my lover still had a strong erection. We had just started experimenting with avoiding orgasm during sex, so I asked him, "isn't that making you uncomfortable?" I could hear a big smile in his voice, as he replied, "no, I love it!" And when we woke up during the night, I found out why....   *Kaiya*

Masturbation is fueled by our familiar sense of deprivation. As one friend explained: "Others are getting pleasure I'm not, so I just look after myself." Unfortunately this sense of emotional isolation too often becomes a self-perpetuating cycle. The uneasiness that follows orgasm can cause you to hide in your cave—even if you think you really want a partner. As a German friend (who masturbated very frequently) put it:

Thanks for your advice, but I cannot conjure a woman out of a cylinder like a rabbit...I'm still kind of wary thinking of women anyway... Why should I give up the cozy privacy of my apartment for a strenuous woman??

His apartment was cramped, barren and dominated by his computer with its various pornography subscriptions. A tomb provides refuge but has its limitations. The bottom line? The more you retreat into your own private world of self-gratification and self-pity the less likely you are to attract a lover. Petulant inertia is not appealing to prospective partners.

Union with another person offers the potential for satisfaction that managing our sexual energy alone can't offer. At a deep level we all know this. Otherwise we "do-it- yourselfers" wouldn't even be reading a book on relationships—our needs would be met. One man I spoke with had put it all together: "I know that when I have the uncontrollable need to masturbate, it's because I've passed up an opportunity to connect deeply with someone."

As we'll see in the next chapter, medical research has confirmed that caring touch from another actually decreases the stress hormones your body pumps into you when, for example, you feed it angry, despairing messages. So if you've been a solo performer for a while, declare an intermission, and then try a duet. Meanwhile, find a massage therapist.

A break in the action can have its own rewards. When I visited Findhorn, a spiritual community in Scotland, returning visitors complained that the spiritual feelings they had experienced during earlier workshops would fade after they got home. A 19 year old Scot helped me see that part of the "magic of Findhorn" was probably the unaccustomed abstinence of its visitors. As my friend put it, he suffered from "Find-horniness" while he was there because he had to share a room for the week with another man whom he'd never met. And he was busy with touchy-feely group activities each day. The combination took masturbation out of the picture for the week of the workshop. And he felt wonderful until soon after he got home—when his depressions and lack of focus mysteriously returned.

> When I went away to university I began masturbating about four times a day. My paranoia level grew so high that once, when someone said, "Good Morning, Scott," I remember wondering, "What did he *really* mean by that?" I also started using drugs a lot and dropped out after my first year. *Scott*

Meanwhile What Do I Do?

If you wish to attract a partner in order to try this new approach, you need the magnetic charge you would lose in masturbation. So for a month, at least, view masturbation as something you stop in order to increase your personal magnetism. Meanwhile, what do you do if you're bursting with life force energy, have met a potential partner you haven't connected with yet, or can't sleep? Here are some techniques others have found helpful:

- do movement work, martial arts, dancing, yoga, tai chi or some other disciplined practice
- consciously circulate your sexual energy whenever you feel uncomfortably aroused. See the "Energy Circulation" in the introduction to the first *Phase* of the *Exchanges*.
- do some spiritual work to open your heart and heal any lingering resentments.
- exchange loving attention with the opposite sex even before your next partner appears. Start by giving. Invite a close friend of the opposite sex to take a walk. Give a foot massage with no strings attached. Hug a lot. Do a friend an unsolicited favor. Such actions not only guarantee that nice things come back to you, they also give you something productive to do with your pent-up sexual energy. As it flows outward in selfless service you'll find your tensions are relieved while your heart stays open.

> The only time I can stop masturbating is when I'm in a relationship. *Andy*

If you can't completely stop having orgasms while on your own, don't get discouraged. When I'm celibate for long periods of time, I sort of run down. I tend to get colds, feel more anxious, accomplish less, and eventually have dream orgasms. Male friends report that they just get hornier and hornier until they eventually relieve themselves or work themselves into exhaustion.

Even a rigorous spiritual practice is no guarantee of successful abstinence. One of my friends did Transcendental Meditation for years and was also without a partner. He noticed that his practice would take him to higher and higher states of bliss. Yet, after some weeks, his sexual energy would start to make him feel like he was going crazy. So he'd masturbate and feel better for about a week.

By the second week, however, panic attacks would begin. Once he heard that radioactive waste was being disposed of in plastic and got the idea that his foam rubber pillow was going to cause cancer. He lay awake for nights. No logic would comfort him; he lived a nightmare. After a week of such distress, though, he'd begin to laugh at his fear. Then he'd feel better and better until the next cycle. For years he's avoided the only cure: union. He feels too fragile, too locked in his private world of meditation and masturbation, to enter a relationship.

It's easy to conclude he has other issues, but I have seen radical improvements in levels of confidence, self-esteem and paranoia in friends who have cut back on this seemingly harmless habit. In any case, I'm convinced that some of us are here to learn about the synergy that lies in union. So if abstinence isn't working for you, despite lofty goals and means, then find someone to love and try managing your sexual energy in a new way.

Meanwhile, you could experiment with increasing your self-discipline. If you have an orgasm how long is it until your next one in the form of a dream orgasm, or wet dream? You might use that interval as the basis of a schedule. The Taoists also propose ejaculation schedules for men that vary depending upon age and season of the year. And an Edgar Cayce reading recommended a hiatus of six to eight weeks.[16] In any case here's a handy "rule of hand." If the sign below looks fuzzy to you increase the intervals between self-pleasuring rituals.

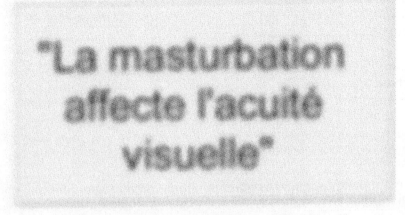

Translation: "Masturbation affects visual acuity"
[Belgian humor from the Internet]

After all, what do you have to lose by changing your habits for a while and seeing how you feel? As one friend said, "it costs nothing, and at worst I pass up a few genital orgasms." If you do decide to cut back, make it easy for yourself; get rid of your vibrator, avoid dwelling on titillating sexual thoughts, and stop mentally undressing others. Resolutely steer clear of all romance novels, pornography and movies with heavy sex. Such pastimes are powerful triggers, and create a sense of deprivation and defensiveness—whether or not you masturbate all the way to orgasm.

TIP: When you *do* get close to a partner, don't assume you will have more control if you masturbate first. Masturbation destabilizes you—and lowers your sights. Try the slow, effortless approach recommended in the *Exchanges* instead.

Now that you have some background in the unsuspected perils of the way we currently handle our innate sexual frustration, let's look at some more benefits of the alternative.

38

Chapter 3
A Change of Heart

I am a forty-four year old woman. Five years ago I was in a serious car accident and suffered a head trauma injury. Six months into recovery I was in yet another collision. I was put on heavy medications for pain and sleeplessness. I took Vicodin®, Prozac®, Ambien® and regular injections of Imetrex® in large amounts daily.

I saw a dramatic, unwelcome change in myself as a result of my dependency on these prescription drugs. I was in a situation over which I had no control. To escape my prescription prison I tried hypnotherapy, physiotherapy, psychotherapy and acupuncture...all to no avail.

Some months ago I met a kind and loving man who practices your program. He felt that with the right kind of energy and balance I would no longer need these drugs. I admit I was very skeptical, but also touched by his concern. I was willing to try.

I have never been happier. It has been over five months and I have completely stopped ALL medications. My life once again has balance, rhythm and clarity. Thank you for helping make this possible. My new drug of choice is "No Orgasm" and I am sharing your website with everyone I care about.   *Julianne*

Do we really have the power to help each other heal simply by learning to make love without drive toward conventional orgasm? Yes. Caring intimacy strengthens and heals as surely as cravings, discord and isolation promote illness.

For now, though, biology has us hooked into a sexual pleasure/reward addiction that's not unlike a substance addiction—with equally predictable hangover and withdrawal symptoms. This addiction's worst fallout is the selfishness and emotional separation it promotes. In the next chapter we'll look more closely at the body chemistry behind these unhealthy consequences of our blind search for physical gratification.

Happily, consciously putting the well-being of another first is the perfect defense against the impulsive commands of our primitive brains. When we shift our focus to openhearted nurturing we produce a body chemistry that is balanced, life enhancing, and non-addictive. These good feelings keep the sparkle in our intimacy. They also still cravings—even the yen for conventional orgasm, alcohol or drugs. The familiar struggle to have our needs met disappears from our unions. How does this work?

Cuddle Hormones

Let's start with the heart. The heart, it turns out, is full of surprises. You probably remember it as an organ that pumps blood. That it is, but scientists have recently learned it's also a gland. That is, it produces various hormones, one of which is called oxytocin. Known as, "the cuddle hormone," oxytocin is associated with selfless nurturing and deep bonding. Nursing mothers generate high levels of it, but everyone produces it when their hearts feel open and loving.

For example, oxytocin levels increase during activities like massage, kissing and intercourse. And it literally helps couples bond, too, as it aids in erection of the penis and encourages female sexual receptivity. It was once believed that oxytocin was produced only in the pituitary gland, but the heart can produce it in quantities at least as great. So that loving feeling you sometimes get in your heart is anything but imaginary.

If it weren't for oxytocin I suspect few of us would ever seek intimacy again following bruises from a broken relationship. Oxytocin promotes a desire to interact with others through comforting and seeking comfort. It dissolves the defensiveness and tendency to seek isolation that our subconscious fears of intimacy have left us with. Studies show women produce more of it than men, which makes women more likely to seek comfort under stress, than to flee or fight. But, in my experience, men can consistently produce just as much "bonding juice" as women when they do not use sex in such a way that it leads to uneasiness about ongoing intimacy. In fact, scientists have discovered that males can produce more of another bonding hormone, vasopressin, which seems to increase their attentiveness to their mates by helping them learn and remember.[17]

> I believe that sex is one of the most beautiful, natural, wholesome things that money can buy.   *Steve Martin*

Vermin Love

A few years back neurochemists began studying two species of vole (a mouse-like rodent). In one species, the prairie vole, males and females mate monogamously for life as soon as they have sex, and highly value the companionship of their mates. The montane vole, however, is promiscuous and ambivalent about company. It turns out that these differences in behavior are associated with the hormones the voles produce and the different cell receptors to which those hormones bind.

> ### Neurochemistry in a Nutshell
> Nerve cells have multiple receptors on their surfaces. The receptors are like exclusive docks, each specially designed to receive only certain neurochemical messengers. When a neurochemical, say a hormone, is released into the body, it docks in multiple receptors on nerve cells designed to receive it. When enough neurochemicals bind to a cell's receptors, the nerve cell is stimulated. If it's a pain nerve cell, for example, it won't send you a pain message until the density of pain-related neurochemicals docked on its surface reaches a certain threshold.
>
> It is almost impossible to talk about the effects of neurochemicals without over simplifying the reality. All are necessary and most have multiple functions in our body depending upon where they bind and in what quantities. For example, the effects of oxytocin that cause a woman to become
> *[continued...]*

41

sexually receptive are binding to receptors in the pleasure section of the brain. When they bind elsewhere they may cause her to lactate or give birth. The key to well-being seems to be maintaining an *ideal balance.* So if you're thinking it would be nice just to pop an oxytocin pill to bond, forget it. In any event, as we'll see in Chapter 4, your body has unpleasant ways of coping with artificial excesses of bliss.

But back to voles. Oxytocin appears to be one key to the prairie voles' monogamy. For example, prairie vole females injected with chemicals that blocked the effects of their oxytocin before mating did *not* develop any sort of bond afterward with obviously distressed and confused males. But cell receptors for hormones also play a part. For example, vasopressin, the hormone that makes male prairie voles so devoted, only causes montane vole males to groom themselves more. One theory is that the vasopressin binds to different nerve cells in the two species.

I wonder whether these hormones also bond to different receptors in humans, depending upon an individual's openness to intimacy. I've noticed that when people get discouraged about seeking intimacy they—like the montane vole—tend to comfort themselves exclusively, becoming more and more self-absorbed. It may be that when we grow despondent about intimacy certain receptors on our cells hibernate. When we find a new sense of optimism about relationships we may unconsciously activate these dormant receptors and produce more neurochemicals that promote bonding. This shift would explain why people who have tried this other approach to sex discover an elation about getting closer that simply wasn't formerly in their repertoire.

In short, some of us can't even accurately assess our potential for fulfilling intimacy until we take the first steps toward promoting different body chemistry by adopting a new behavior. For example, recent research suggests that a solid intimate relationship enhances the benefits of oxytocin in women (men did not participate in this study). Women who were currently involved in a stable relationship experienced greater emotional highs in response to massage and artificially induced positive stimuli, and showed less depression in response to negative stimuli. Those without partners responded less strongly to the "highs" and were more depressed by the emotional "lows." [18]

Incidentally the researchers in that study weren't even looking at the effects of relationship on well-being—until they noticed that women were responding radically differently to oxytocin-stimulating activities. Then they administered psychological tests that revealed the deciding factor was a stable relationship. In other words, hormone levels are as much a reflection of our inner state as they are a cause. And a sense of inner balance—impossible to achieve while riding the relationship roller coaster or feeling lonely—may be critical to ideal hormone levels. The point is that you have the potential to produce a body chemistry that feels great and is not addictive. And it comes from closeness and a sense of wholeness, not orgasm.

Up until now, we, like the vole, have unconsciously been directed by our instincts. But unlike the vole, we are not at biology's mercy. We have a choice. We are starting to learn which emotions and behaviors produce a balanced body chemistry of well-being. To profit from this knowledge we must be willing to override the commands of our primitive brains.

For now, conventional sex has left many of us feeling like isolationist, montane voles. Yet we are not so self-sufficient. Nearly half of all Americans literally die of broken hearts (cardiovascular disease). As we'll see in a moment, intimacy and companionship are unquestionably better for our well-being…if we can maintain them harmoniously.

Sorry, Chocolate Lovers
If you've ever had a crush you know how different you feel. Those amazing feelings are heavily associated with PEA, a form of norepinephrine. This hormone causes your body to release bursts of energy. Indeed, PEA relieves depression in many and often leads to improvements in energy levels, attention and mood.   *[continued…]*

Chocolate also contains PEA, and it has a reputation as a "substitute for love." Unfortunately digestion breaks down chocolate's PEA before it can energize you. So chocolate, alas, is a false substitute. Chocolate's lift comes from hangover-prone ingredients like caffeine and sugar.

What Can Harmonious Union Do for You?

Decades of research have firmly established that a stable, happy marriage is the best defense against illness and premature death.[19] In a seven-year study of 800 young adults, depression and alcohol abuse declined more significantly for those who married during that time.[20] And, the prejudices of the moral majority notwithstanding, co-habitors, too, enjoy significantly lower levels of psychological distress than individuals with no partner or those with a partner living outside the household.[21]

To be sure, it's not the marriage certificate or shared address that protects you. Indeed, as we'll see in Chapter 6 both marital disharmony and divorce correlate with poorer health. So the benefits of union hinge on couples maintaining a degree of harmony.[22] Science has begun to measure the gifts of togetherness that lie in companionship, touch, and sexual intimacy. Here are some interesting findings:

- Studies done over two decades involving more than thirty-seven thousand people show that social isolation—the sense that you have nobody with whom you can share your private feelings or have close contact—doubles the chances of sickness or death.[23]

- Closeness increases the likelihood of touch—and caring touch (rather than eager fondling) may be the greatest of intimacy's potential gifts. It has powerful health benefits. It helps you heal faster and resist illness. For HIV-positive men, one month of regular massage significantly strengthened their embattled immune systems.[24] Selfless touch increases the natural release of serotonin, which reduces irritability and cravings. So touch not only helps reduce addiction, it may naturally decrease the urge to ejaculate. For example, Prozac® users, who have artificially increased levels of serotonin, often experience delayed ejaculation. Touch also allows you to sleep more easily by reducing levels of adrenaline and other stress hormones.[25]

- In 1997, *The British Medical Journal* reported a long-term study of chronic disease in men. "Sexual activity seems to have a protective effect on men's health," said Dr. George Davey-Smith. Having sex twice per week appears to reduce the risk of death for men by half (compared with those who had sex once a month). Incidentally, "ejaculation enthusiasts" often cite this study as proof that regular orgasm is good for men, but the more than 900 study participants (age 45-59 at the beginning of a 10 year study) were generally engaged in regular intimate contact with long-term female partners. Ejaculation and masturbation weren't isolated as control factors; only sex with a partner was. So the study probably tells us more about the benefits of regular intimate contact than the benefits of ejaculation alone.[26]

- For women, *enjoyment* of intercourse is associated with longer life.[27] There is also less heart disease in women who are more satisfied with the quality of their sex lives.[28]

As Dean Ornish explained in *Love and Survival,*[29] love and intimacy are such powerful determinants of health that if they came in drug form, doctors who failed to prescribe them would unquestionably be guilty of malpractice. Behaviors that connect us with others in a genuinely caring way have an even greater beneficial impact on our health than regular exercise, stopping smoking or improved diet. For example, a study was done of almost ten thousand married men with chest pain (angina). Among those with high risk factors (elevated cholesterol, high blood pressure, age, diabetes and irregular heartbeat), there was almost twice as much angina in the group of men who answered, "No" to the question, "Does your wife show you her love?"[30]

Science is also beginning to measure the benefits of intimacy's less tangible aspects, such as the benefits that come from caring about another. In a study of 700 elderly adults, researchers found that what people contributed reduced the effects of aging more than what they received from others.[31] And volunteers not only tend to live longer, but even report bursts of joyful feelings when helping others.[32] It is easy to see how this joy from giving can carry over into the bedroom allowing you and your lover to feel fulfilled and bond more deeply.

HeartMath, a research institute, has demonstrated that consciously choosing openhearted emotions of caring, compassion, and appreciation can have measurable health benefits[33]. After a month, people who were taught to substitute these positive feelings for feelings of anger and frustration showed significant beneficial changes in key hormone levels.

This is big news for your health. In response to these positive emotions, cortisol levels dropped. Cortisol is known as the "stress hormone" because it is secreted in excessive amounts when we are under stress. At the same time DHEA levels increased. DHEA is known as the "anti-aging hormone" because it enhances the immune system, stimulates bone deposition, lowers cholesterol levels and builds muscle mass.

A good DHEA/cortisol ratio improves your chances of warding off a host of severe health problems associated with unfavorable (that is, lower DHEA/higher cortisol) ratios. Such problems include increased fat accumulation, decreased skin repair and regeneration, elevated blood sugar levels, increased bone loss, compromised immune function, and brain cell destruction. So relationship harmony that enables us to keep our hearts open may prove to be a fountain of youth, the ultimate diet, and an all-purpose healing tonic.

> **Three weeks after we began the *Exchanges*, my libido started to return. In the months since, my health has steadily improved, my energy level has risen, and my sexual desire has continued to increase. I'm happy. My friends comment that I'm glowing and look 10-15 years younger.** *Ellen*

Indeed, the ancient Chinese Taoists prescribed hours of non-orgasmic sex in various positions as cures for a host of diseases. Imagine doctors' prescriptions reading, *"Patient must stay home and make love all day for serious health reasons."* Even better than a handicapped parking sticker!

The Taoists also claimed that correct mutual cultivation of sexual energy could lead to immortality. So it's especially intriguing that the "anti-aging hormone," DHEA, is closely linked to our sexual health. This hormone is the precursor to the human sex hormones estrogen and testosterone. In short, if you want to feel young and sexy, shift your focus to nurturing your partner with an open heart—and ignore biology's fertilization behavior commands.

"I've heard men can develop prostate trouble from not ejaculating."

This widespread belief began when a study revealed that priests have a disproportionately high rate of prostate trouble. (Gay men, by the way, have a lower than average incidence of prostate trouble.) I tracked the priest study down in a medical library. It turns out that prostate trouble is a function of "congestion," which is stagnant blood (in this case, in the prostate region). So frequent activity that moves the blood in that region—not ejaculation itself—is the key to prostate health. *[R.K. Ross, et al., "A Cohort Study of Mortality from Cancer of the Prostate in Catholic Priests,"; British Journal of Cancer (1981), Vol. 43: 2, 233-235.]*

With the approach to lovemaking recommended in this book, lovers tend to make love for longer periods of time and more often—without becoming uncomfortably over-aroused. Also, erections come and go, which gently pumps blood through the entire prostate region. Skeptical men have checked with their urologists, who have confirmed that ejaculation is not necessary for good prostate health.

Synching Up

Openheartedness is not merely an aid in bonding deeply and a means of staying youthful, fit and more resistant to disease. The heart has yet another hidden talent. It generates the strongest electromagnetic field that the body produces. HeartMath, the research institute mentioned above, has shown that this field becomes measurably more coherent as we shift to sincerely loving or caring states. "Coherence" is an indication of inner balance. It means our body systems are working especially well together. It correlates with increased immunity, better cognitive ability (that is, we think more clearly), and the capacity to handle stress more easily with greater flexibility. Our bodies clearly like equilibrium.

Best of all, a coherent electromagnetic heart field may be the key to truly remarkable states of union. When we are in a loving, coherent state our heartbeat can even register in another's brainwaves. This potential for synchronizing electromagnetic fields when in a loving state may account for the Taoist "Valley Orgasm" experience in which lovers sense a profound merging that leaves them tingling with well-being for days or weeks.

HeartMath has yet to do any research on comparing different approaches to sex. However, Rollin McCraty, Director of Research at HeartMath Institute, told me that he once measured the heart rate coherence over a 24-hour period for a number of couples attending a tantra workshop. He found that there was an unexpectedly high incidence of synchronization between some of the lovers—especially while they were sleeping. As you will see, the recipe in the second half of this book begins with sleeping together. Experience has shown that this gentle contact has very beneficial effects, some of which may come from this unconscious synchronization between open hearts.

> We've been practicing making love for several months this other way, and I haven't ejaculated once. I feel a lot better. I no longer have any guilt about sex, or worry about my performance. It makes me feel good to be so relaxed with her,
>
> *[continued...]*

without anxiety. **During intercourse, we go for a little while and just relax together, and then repeat the cycle over and over. My health and my sense of well-being have changed for the better. I've quit drinking and cut way back on smoking. I have no back pain, heartburn, headaches or elbow pain anymore. I'm sleeping better, and don't have frightening dream images like I had before.** *Mike*

Partner Pampering

Try for a moment to feel *love* and *hate* at the same time. You can't. In fact, there is no middle ground between an open heart and a closed one, and very different body chemistry accompanies each. This means the cure for unhealthy defensiveness is not neutrality, or even negotiated fairness. It is active caring or giving. You have to move your attention outward to reap the benefits of an open heart.

It is thus impossible to mix the reward seeking of conventional sex with the approach advocated in this book—and see lasting benefits. If we don't consistently tap the body chemistry gifts of openhearted caring in our relationships we're stuck in neutral. We naturally tend to seek even harder for passionate excitement. Ultimately biology succeeds in pushing us back into conventional orgasm—and a downward spiral.

Giving is the best defense against impulsive behavior. You may have forgotten how wonderful it feels to care for your partner selflessly because conventional sex so swiftly makes relationships mutually draining—a phenomenon we'll examine more closely in the next chapter. Draining, of course, is what makes us defensive and unenthusiastic about giving. This biological selfishness has haunted us for a long time.

Compromise
Adam was walking around the Garden of Eden feeling very lonely, so God asked Adam, "What is wrong with you?" Adam said
[continued...]

he didn't have anyone to talk to. God said he was going to give him a companion and it would be a woman. God said, "This person will cook for you and wash your clothes, she will always agree with every decision you make. She will bear your children, and never ask you to get up in the middle of the night to take care of them. She will not nag you, and will always be the first to admit she was wrong when you've had a disagreement. She will never have a headache, and will freely give you love and passion whenever needed."

Adam asked God, "What will a woman like this cost?" God said, "An arm and a leg." "Well...," said Adam, "what could I get for just a rib?"

No Compromise

If they can put a man on the moon, they ought to be able to put 'em all up there.   *The Internet*

The good news is that giving swiftly becomes natural when you make love without this drain. Why? It feels good. Your partner's joy is yours as well. Mutual caring creates a profound feeling of comfort and a sense of abundance. Old fears of intimacy simply cannot withstand this deep sense of mutual security, so they fade away.

Focusing your attention on making your partner feel loved is also a reliable aphrodisiac. While traditional foreplay is often about "purchasing" sex—and eventually leaves someone unhappy with the bargain—a loving head rub or foot rub, without expectations, is truly a gift. Genuine gifts call forth a spontaneous receptivity and desire for merging from your partner—and that is always a turn on.

A friend in England who experimented with a variation of the *Exchanges* found that soon she enthusiastically initiated sex with her husband—which he relished. For years she'd grimly endured intercourse—which she had found painful—just to hold her marriage together. "And," she confided in her colorful Cockney accent, "Ee *loved* ees foot massage. In twenty-foive years of marriage oi'd never even *seen* ees feet!"

LIZ ESTRATA

When you take the biological goal of conventional orgasm out of sex it
frees you to approach each other more selflessly. It's heartening to know
your partner is looking out for you and has the boundless energy of a
teen to do it. You can also explore new heights of intimacy when you
can both surrender in safety. Effortlessness pervades relationships built
on this foundation. There's no performance anxiety, and, obviously, no
pressure on either lover to deliver an orgasm to please a partner.

The healing that follows this simple change of heart from "what can I
get?" to "what can I give?" will truly amaze you. Setbacks that would be
cause for outrage if you were thinking of your partnership as a "deal,"
are only cause for compassion and assistance if your motivation is truly
to comfort and heal. Needless to say, we recover far more rapidly
without recrimination or guilt in the mix.

It is impossible to appreciate fully the peace of mind and increase in
well-being that accompanies this approach until you try it for an
extended period. At first, though, you will need a very slow,
conservative approach to sexual intimacy. Remember when you learned
to ride a bicycle? At first it was nerve wracking, but you soon came to
love the feeling of perfect balance, freedom and control. When this new
approach becomes automatic, sexual arousal will no longer demand
frantic fertilization efforts. Instead it will feel like an invitation to enter
into a steady state of delicious, satisfying lovemaking that has a timeless,
fulfilling, eternal quality to it. Best of all, you can produce the body
chemistry that accompanies it indefinitely. It's far better for you than the
explosive, imbalanced body chemistry we'll look at next.

> At first when I realized my lover was more generous than I was
> I felt like the right answer was for her to give less. I see now
> that that would have slowly strangled the relationship by
> setting up a constant negotiation about who was doing more.
> I'm glad I discovered true giving. I feel stronger, more
> confident and more...connected to the universal flow. The
> more I give, the more comes my way—from everywhere. *Bruce*

51

Chapter 4
Outwitting Biology

A friend recently emailed me a vision of his ideal woman. Here's *half* of it:

The woman I marry is the most beautiful in the world. She is 5'6", slender, with brown hair and hazel eyes. She has the face of a madonna and the personality to match. She never lies and cares deeply about everyone. She makes a great chicken casserole even though she is vegetarian. She is comforter, provider and mother to those in need. She sees goodness and beauty in everything and bears no ill will toward anyone. She is patience incarnate. She makes people happier just by being around them.

The woman of my dreams is wonderful, fun to be with and stunningly attractive. She is completely at ease with herself and in harmony with all that is. A gift from God, she is warm, gentle, loving, compassionate, generous, open and graceful. She is confident, wise, and intelligent.

She has a great sense of humor and can drive a stick shift. She likes exploring new things but is content with her achievements. There is no situation she can't cope with. She is never envious or greedy, and she doesn't manipulate others or speak bad about them. She is playful and innocent but streetwise. She has her own mind, but listens to others. She is always smiling. She likes mountaineering and bakes delicious sourdough bread. She loves me deeply and accepts me exactly as I am. She makes me feel safe, like all is right with the world.... I only want to be with *her* for the rest of my life.

Almost everyone has an ideal mate checklist in one form or another. I remember mine. I made it in 1986 after my sister—weary of watching the turnover in my love life—bought me a book entitled something like, *Marrying the Man of Your Choice*. The book was adamant that such a list was vital, so I did my homework...thoroughly. It was ultimately three pages long.

And sure enough the man showed up within a year. Not only that, a couple of months before Russ and I met, a psychic had assured him that he would meet me by a certain date. She'd told him my age, my profession, the element of my astrological sign, and several other surprisingly accurate things. We met at a conference in New York City two days before the date she'd named. To us it truly felt like a heavenly match. Yet, shortly after conventional sex entered the picture the relationship blew apart. And every time we tried again it blew apart again.

I've watched others find ideal mates, too, only to see their relationships crumble before their eyes. I can think of few more painful experiences. One man told me that the only time he seriously contemplated suicide was after such a relationship turned into the most excruciating experience he'd ever been through.

The Right Flow of Energy

So what have we all been overlooking? When my relationship with Russ hit the rocks, I turned to my inner guidance and I asked. The same week I ran into my first Taoist lovemaking book and I sensed it was The Answer. It has taken me years to understand that answer. In the process I have also learned why ideal mate lists are obstacles to true harmony.

Here's the simple truth. You can't build a solid relationship on what you each *want*. Solid relationships are built on what you each *give*. I am not talking about mutual sacrifice or about mutual selfishness— euphemistically known as negotiation. I am talking about a completely different flow of energy between partners than we see in conventional relationships.

A Man's Guide to Female English
- If she says, "I'll be ready in a minute" it means "kick off your shoes and find a good game on TV"
- "I'm not yelling!" means "Yes I'm yelling because I think it's important."
- "All we're going to buy is a soap dish" means "It goes without saying that we're stopping at the cosmetics department, the shoe department, I need to look at a few purses, those sheets would look great in the bedroom... and, did you bring your check book?"
- "Yes" *means* "No"
- "No" *means* "No"
- "Maybe" *means* "No"   *The Internet*

We have taught ourselves to think of our relationships as arm's length deals. An ideal mate list is a catalog of the returns you are looking for on your potential investment. Historically this mentality has been viewed as great wisdom. In fact, until this century, most marriages were arranged for the participants so they wouldn't let romantic nonsense get in the way of more sensible considerations. If there were no hidden potential between open hearts, such logic would make perfect sense. There's logic behind selfless giving in relationships, too. Here's an even more reliable returns principle than making deals: what you give out will return to you.

In short, the only way you will feel satisfied, safe and loved is if you offer these gifts to your partner unconditionally. See your interests as equally important to both of you. Think of yourselves as two hands of one entity. There need not be a defensive sense of separation even though you are in two bodies. This shift toward a unified perception may take awhile, but it requires surprisingly little effort when you consistently use this approach to lovemaking.

To be sure, mutual selflessness is a very high standard of conduct. And I suspect it's impossible to maintain with conventional sex in the picture.

While biology drives us we just don't have the energy to put another first. The inherent chemical blasts and hangovers from passion create an artificial sense of deprivation. When we project it outward either we feel like we're sacrificing (being drained) by others or we feel a need to defend or protect ourselves. As we saw in the last chapter such heart closing emotions equate with higher levels of stress hormones and decreased amounts of anti-aging and desire-to-bond hormones.

Pleasure/Reward Addiction

So if selfless love offers so many benefits how does biology sucker us into repeatedly undermining or (eventually) avoiding relationships? If I had to answer that question in two words I would say, "dopamine blasts." Dopamine is the neurochemical, or hormone, most closely associated with reward and addiction. It rewards you for engaging in certain activities by acting on nerve cells in a part of the brain located in the limbic system, or primitive brain.

At ideal levels dopamine helps you maintain a sense of well-being by steadily stimulating your pleasure center. But when you deliberately trigger its overproduction you generate a burst of ecstasy followed by a crash. You can overdose on such things as cocaine, amphetamines, alcohol, or conventional orgasm. These forced jolts of pleasure are highly addictive so the axiom "moderation in all things" doesn't necessarily apply to them. One dopamine blast creates the craving for another...and so on.

Such excesses have detrimental repercussions. For example, when receptors on nerve cells are bombarded by stimulants like cocaine, the cells seek to protect themselves against damage from over stimulation by *down regulating*. That is, they deactivate some of their receptors for the type of neurochemical that is flooding them. And once that deactivation occurs, it lingers awhile. This means that even when your dopamine levels return to normal (which may not happen right away because a dopamine blast may temporarily deplete your body's reserves), your pleasure center nerve cells can't pick up enough neurochemical signals to stimulate a response. They have too few activated receptors.

To most of us this perfectly natural, temporary absence of pleasure sensations feels like severe depression. At a body chemistry level the joy has literally gone out of our lives—and it feels like it will never return. We may experience this phenomenon as a sense of despair, anger or an intense craving for anything that can guarantee us a dose of dopamine sufficient to stimulate our pleasure nerves again.

So it is that addictions worsen and are so often mutually reinforcing. When a post-orgasm hangover interferes with our well-being (or unhealthy isolation leaves us feeling joyless), we reach for a drink or a drug or another orgasm, and so on. Sadly, the more we force a sense of well-being by such means, the more we undermine our body's ability to keep us on the even keel that promotes vitality and raises our spirits.

Cold Turkey

All this neurochemistry adds up to one vital insight. If you want to protect your relationship by learning to make love differently, avoid the passion trigger completely. Otherwise you set off a dopamine blast and hangover—or a severe, uncomfortable craving. This will temporarily stop all your progress toward teaching your body to produce an alternative, more balanced combination of "feel good chemicals."

If, instead, you avoid that passionate rush, and turn your attention instead to caring for each other, you won't feel your withdrawal from these dopamine rushes so acutely. You will flood your system with the body chemistry that accompanies selflessness and promotes bonding. Soon you will have built dependable neural pathways for intimacy that feels great without producing a hangover of emotional separation. Your longing for a dopamine rush will noticeably decrease.

This decrease in cravings is perfectly natural. Rats who were first addicted to heroin (that they could administer to themselves at any time),

56

and then treated with oxytocin (the "cuddle hormone"), showed a marked decrease in heroin use. Oxytocin also lessened various effects of cocaine-addicted rats.[34] And if you happen to be partnered with a human you may be interested to know that friends and I who have experimented with this other approach to sex have watched our lovers stop addictions effortlessly. Indeed this hidden potential in harmonious couplehood may offer new encouragement for those facing some otherwise depressing statistics. 70 percent of chronic problem drinkers are either divorced or separated. Single men are more than three times as likely as married men to die of cirrhosis of the liver.[35] Sexual relationships that heal can do much to improve these statistics.

Of course, when you begin this new approach you are still addicted to sex as a dopamine rush trigger. Like an alcoholic entering a 12 Step Program you need to take it one day at a time with an attitude of easy does it. And avoid that "first drink" by skipping the hot foreplay. In other words, the *Exchanges* are not sex as usual, but without orgasm. They comprise a path to a different kind of ecstasy completely—one that does not make us into selfish addicts.

Amygdala as Guardian

The chemical hangover excess dopamine causes isn't the only fallout from forced pleasure jolts. There is a very powerful emotional component to the hangovers and it remains, like a rusty but fully operational bear trap, even when you stop the behavior that forces ecstasy. This is because your amygdala, the part of your primitive brain that archives emotional memories, has carefully recorded that these dopamine highs are followed by miserable lows. Its job is to protect you against repeating past errors. So it sends you a gut feeling of uneasiness when you get close to anything it has associated with painful past events.

Most of us subconsciously come to associate ongoing sexual intimacy with frequent dopamine hangovers. So your amygdala may already have begun to send you fear messages when you approach anyone with whom you could actually form a compatible, *ongoing* relationship. Indeed, the

57

amygdala issues its warnings chemically, and so quickly that they can activate your body's defense reactions before your neo-cortex (the part of your brain that analyzes logically) even has a chance to evaluate a new acquaintance.[36] While the amygdala is guarding you from ongoing intimacy suitable partners just won't turn you on—and you won't even bother to question your verdict.

Mysteriously, however, you will find partners with *Exit* signs flashing behind their heads very attractive. I call this the *Intensity Junkie Syndrome*. If you have become an Intensity Junkie, you can thank your amygdala for your fixation on non-relationships.

Are You An Intensity Junkie?

Do you find yourself consistently choosing partners
- **whom you find when you (or they) are far away from home?**
- **who are married to others?**
- **who dumped you abruptly before?**
- **whom you can only see for brief encounters due to their professional or parental commitments?**
- **who have a long history of brief affairs?**

Do you fall in love with each such partner and have intense romantic encounters?

If you answer *yes* to these two questions you are likely to be an Intensity Junkie. You've already figured out that sex with your heart open is an experience far superior to just having sex. But your subconscious is still fearful of ongoing intimacy because of the associated hangovers.

- **Your "solution" is to predetermine an escape route that your subconscious believes will allow you to elude the inevitable fallout. And so you are fearless during the encounter and easily open your heart. Indeed, an Intensity Junkie can have orgasms that *feel* like**

[continued]

---

profound spiritual experiences, and are as compelling as mainlining heroin. They have all the drawbacks, too:

- They create hangovers, even if your subconscious doesn't register the cause and effect link. Though your mystical encounter may remain untarnished in your mind, your life will reflect back to you your sense of lack. Frequently it shows up in the form of disappointment, illness, depression, poverty, etc.
- You can't master sexual self-control in fleeting, intense encounters. First, you haven't built up the balance and inner strength that makes control a real possibility, and second, the temptation to go for orgasm is usually overpowering when you're not likely to see each other again (or any time soon).
- And, as an Intensity Junkie you are hooked on non-relationships. In fact, you can't get your accustomed high in a relationship with possible commitment looming.

It may take time, but "Intensity Junkie" gradually leads to stagnation. You're always planning your escape or feeling victimized by departing lovers. Your will is actually imprisoned by your defenses. And, like any other addict, you're not inclined to go through an unsatisfying withdrawal period in favor of forming real relationships. Why? Because they won't meet your craving for the "great sex" you're hooked on. To feel those highs again, you must learn to open your heart in situations where commitment is a real possibility—and that will take some time and mutual healing.

Whether or not you're an Intensity Junkie, if you are hooked on conventional sex, your best hope for freeing yourself from all vestiges of this biological snare is to avoid the dopamine blast during sex. With time your amygdala will record a new memory of ongoing intimacy. It will come to associate it with an increasing sense of coziness, joy and well-being. In other words, you will gradually create an alternative subconscious programming around intimate relationships.

Take Heart

If the thought of passing up your dopamine rushes is depressing you remember the previous chapter. Just because you give up orgasm doesn't mean you will give up pleasure. As you re-pattern using the *Exchanges* you will be feeling very pampered *and* giving selflessly to your lover. This means your heart and brain will produce a delicious cocktail of body chemicals. Both oxytocin and dopamine itself (at lower levels) are associated with sexual arousal. So you will feel both sexy and loving. You just won't throw your nerve cells or your subconscious into addiction/defensive mode.

Scientists have recognized that conventional sex is linked to a fight-or-flight response. As you may know, the nervous system responds to stimuli in two basic ways. The sympathetic response, which kicks in when you hear screeching tires just behind you, calls high levels of stress hormones into the bloodstream. The parasympathetic response, on the other hand, is known as the relaxation response. It is the ideal gear for most bodily functions—like digestion and regeneration. Sexual arousal is a parasympathetic, relaxation response but ejaculation is a stressful, sympathetic response. I believe this flood of stress hormones accounts for extreme behavior in the emotionally undernourished.

> **Chinese medicine long ago observed that vicious crimes are often committed soon after seminal loss. Courage is usually at low ebb after ejaculation. One scares easily and reacts violently.**[37]

The military appears to exploit this means of increasing violent aggression in soldiers. Both British troops heading to the Falklands and American soldiers before bombing raids during the Gulf War were deliberately shown pornographic videos.

Women are also adversely affected by the jolt from conventional orgasm. And many couples I've talked to notice a tendency to bicker with each other the day after a conventional sexual encounter. I find it comforting that such disharmony may be due entirely to body chemistry shifts we could be avoiding.

With neurochemicals it's seldom possible to say, "this one does this and that one does that." Quantity, openness of receptors on the nerve cells, and the complex interaction of different neurochemicals determine their effects. But something about the right combination of dopamine and oxytocin seems to be vital in turning a neutral sexual experience into a strongly positive and reinforced one that lasts.[38]

In other words, if we can learn to maintain the ideal levels of dopamine, oxytocin and other pleasure neurochemicals (by making *equilibrium* our goal), we can enjoy ongoing sexual intimacy without hangovers. Such an approach may be unfamiliar but it is hardly new. The Taoists noted thousands of years ago that the less passionate path of intercourse can lead to an ecstatic relaxation orgasm (rather than a forced tension-and-release orgasm).

Whether or not you experience a total relaxation orgasm with this gentler approach, you will relish your enhanced inner balance. A profound sense of well-being increases as you move away from the degenerating cycle of highs and lows. And, as your primitive brain relaxes its guard, your heart opens.

WANTED: Meaningful overnight relationship.

If you want a committed lover, look in a mental institution.

The Internet

Uncharacteristic Behavior

We've reviewed some chemical and emotional effects of addiction, but it has other side effects worth emphasizing. The initial ecstatic feelings that accompany dopamine rushes make us very goal driven; watch any rat that gets a reward when it completes a learned behavior. In our case this dopamine rush is biology's reward for engaging in fertilization behavior. When we are focused on attaining such a powerful reward, we have very little attention or energy for anything else. So, if genital friction leads to the fastest orgasm, we will find ourselves more and more driven to engage in it. We simply won't see the point in any other type of contact. Indeed, when addiction holds sway, the more you get, the more you want. Pretty soon neither your well-being nor your lover's is as important to you as getting your fix.

Here's an extreme example. A friend of mine had severe urinary tract infection during the months following her marriage. She and her husband both liked sex and by the time she was in severe pain, urinating blood, her husband was so hooked on orgasm that he informed her he was demanding his "marital rights" at least three times a week regardless of her condition. I suspect her acute condition was in part related to her hurt feelings about the increasing insensitivity of this man she loved. But their problems arose quite innocently. And he was not alone in his shortsightedness; she loved the role of seductress. For example, during their courtship—while she lived in another city—she'd often sent him nude pictures of herself over the Internet to warm him up.

If you pour lighter fluid on sexual desire you pretty much guarantee a biological stampede. Yet greed—and resentment—destroy relationships. Such reactions occur involuntarily while biology drives us, but the repercussions can be ugly. If we were thinking more clearly we'd never do some of the hurtful and self-sacrificing things we do under the influence of this addiction to orgasm.

Incidentally, years ago I took antibiotics almost every time I made love to avoid urinary tract infection. I haven't used them in over 10 years with this approach to lovemaking. And a friend with genital herpes, who experimented with this approach, noticed that outbreaks did not occur except when he wandered back into a search for passion. Less stress means better health.

Less stress also means more durable relationships. When you use someone (or allow them to use you) your mindset distorts your vision of him/her. You begin to perceive your interests as separate. It feels like you're locked in a power struggle. The relationship takes on a suffocating quality. It is the nature of dopamine blasts to leave us feeling threatened and suffering from a sense of lack. When so affected, we naturally tend to think only about ourselves. Our hearts close, radically changing our body chemistry.

This shutdown at the heart level is the highest price we pay for allowing our primitive brains to run our love lives. We usually become selfish or hopelessly judgmental. We feel like someone is making unreasonable demands or like we're victims of someone else's impossible behavior. We have a powerful urge to separate—to protect ourselves. The cure is to open our hearts with generous actions or find compassion for each other, but it's nearly impossible to move our energy out through the heart while the brain chemistry that accompanies conventional sex is creating stress at a physical level. Instead we contract defensively.

You may be thinking that sexual frustration itself is stressful. It is. But don't assume that you will be sexually frustrated simply because you and your partner avoid orgasm. If the solution I'm proposing doesn't heal frustration it's no solution at all. Try the *Exchanges* completely before you evaluate their effectiveness. A deep sense of well-being arises when you stop goal-oriented behavior and just nurture each other. As Taoists discovered thousands of years ago, your body can produce a most satisfying sex life without conventional orgasm.

This realization that your needs are effortlessly being met heals. It gives you the strength to drop defensive patterns you chose in the past such as shutting down emotionally, dissolving into tears, blaming or judging, substance addictions or self-absorption. Gradually you cease to identify with these old behaviors. They weren't *you;* they were just the way you closed your heart when feeling deprived. You begin to see that the cure was always to open your heart and move toward union.

Each time you abandon your defenses in favor of closeness, you will feel your stress level drop instantly. Do your heart a favor.

A Woman's Guide to Male English
- "I'm hungry" *means* "I'm hungry"
- "I'm sleepy" *means* "I'm sleepy"
- "I'm tired" *means* "I'm tired"
- "I love you" *means* "Let's have sex now"
- "I love you, too" *means* "Okay, I said it...we'd better have sex now!"
- "Nice dress" *means* "Nice cleavage!"
- "I like that one better (while shopping) " *means* "Pick any frigging dress and let's go home!"   *The Internet*

Lack

If our ecstasy is linked only to chemical blasts that we engineer, then whenever we're not high we feel like something is missing. Worse yet, our loving feelings are tangled up with artificial, forced jolts of pleasure. So when the inevitable hangovers arrive, and we suddenly feel inexplicably awful, we imagine we have fallen out of love. It seems like our lover doesn't care enough to make us feel good again. Anger and resentment can lead to feelings of hate—or powerful cravings for emotion-numbing substances or activities. This is the recurring seesaw of conventional relationships.

Many of us are familiar with spiritual authorities who warn against the addictiveness of romantic involvement. When you seek outside yourself, they assure us, you are bound to create a painful experience. Such authorities are not envisioning a relationship based on mutual giving. They are envisioning mutual *seeking* (that is, attempts to *get*). This is to be expected because intimate relationships have long revolved around conventional sexual activity—and the selfishness it fuels.

It's easy to see that we will always come up short if we use each other—albeit unintentionally—to create an artificial sense of lack, and then use each other to attempt to fill that very emptiness. Many spiritual traditions have assumed that the only way off the treadmill of empty obsessions and perpetual dissatisfaction is celibacy. Now, however, some spiritual advisors encourage us to stay in our mutually draining relationships until we exceed our pain threshold, separate and devote ourselves to seeking within instead.

I no longer believe the source of our distress is intimate contact with another. The problem is approaching each other while feeling greedy or needy. Our hunger can be due to deprivation or frequent orgasm. Yet a certain longing for wholeness accompanies the simple fact of being one gender or the other. Each of us is, after all, somewhat polarized, like half a magnet.

Once we resolve the situation so that there is no longer a sense of lack associated with union, we are free to discover the synergy and spiritual potential that lies in mutual strengthening. We are still solving the problem from *within,* but not in isolation. We each solve it by balancing and stabilizing our magnetic attraction when we nurture another in a shared experience.

The suggestion that all spiritual work can be done far more efficiently solo (except for painful lessons with each other) is misguided. The return to full spiritual awareness is an experience of the truth that we are all one. A blissful merging with another ego at an energetic level is a very efficient shortcut to a state of mind in which we welcome our oneness with others.

Meanwhile, if you have an ideal mate checklist, lose it. Giving without ulterior motive not only shifts your vision, but also improves your health. No one will look more ideal to you than someone you adore selflessly.

Country Proverb

Before you're married he'll help you over a straw. But after you're married you can find your own way over a haystack.

Chapter 5
Deactivating the *Intimacy Sabotaging Device*

The Marshmallow Challenge

Some years back a group of four year olds were offered the following proposition: "If you wait till I run an errand, you can have two marshmallows. If you can't wait, you can have only one—but you can have it right now." The choices these children made revealed their trajectory through life. According to Daniel Goleman in *Emotional Intelligence*, the capacity to resist impulse is the root of all emotional self-control. The primitive brain acts on reflex while the higher brain sees consequences.

The four year olds who were able to wait resisted temptation by covering their eyes so they wouldn't have to stare at the bait, rested their heads in their arms, talked, sang, played games with their hands and feet, or even tried to sleep. The more impulsive ones grabbed the marshmallow, almost always within seconds of the experimenter's departure on his 20 minute "errand."

Twelve to fourteen years later, the difference between the two groups was dramatic. Those who'd resisted temptation were now more personally effective, self-assertive, and better able to cope with life's frustrations. They were less likely to go to pieces under stress, or become rattled and disorganized when pressured; they pursued challenges even in the face of difficulties; they were self-reliant, confident, trustworthy, dependable and far superior as students— regardless of IQ.

The grabbers, however, were more likely to shy from social contact; to be stubborn and indecisive; to be easily upset by frustration; to think of themselves as "bad" or unworthy; to become immobilized by stress; to be mistrustful and resentful about not getting enough; to be prone to jealousy and envy; to overreact with a sharp temper, provoking arguments and fights—and, they were *still* unable to put off immediate gratification in pursuit of other goals. No doubt, they also masturbated more frequently, bless their hearts.

When it comes to sex we've all been taught to grab for the one marshmallow. Some of us have mastered the use of birth control, and the world-class lovers among us have learned to orchestrate simultaneous orgasms. Yet even our efforts at self-control have revolved around the ultimate objective of grabbing the dopamine blast in the form of conventional orgasm. Thanks to the primitive brain—which can impel sexual behavior and record painful experiences, but does not *consciously choose*—we have not tapped the most precious gifts of sexual self-discipline: healing and harmony. Yet we can choose to recondition the primitive brain to develop a new set of reflexes.

Also, let's face it: tempting as a marshmallow may be to a four year old, it holds little allure compared with an orgasm for most of us. So if you decide to learn to make love this other way, and you like sex, you face a challenge. You must resolutely tune out the insistent signals of your limbic system, which has had the upper hand for a long time when it comes to sexual response.

This can be done, and as you will see if you try the *Exchanges,* I recommend many of the same techniques the savvy four year olds employed. Instead of covering your eyes, you simply keep some clothing on for a while. You, too, distract yourself with carefully chosen activities so you have something to do with your sexual desire other than follow your impulses to their natural conclusion. And you nourish and balance each other by sleeping (just *sleeping*) together. When intercourse enters the picture, you steer around temptation by avoiding vigorous movement. Each *Exchange* also offers a pep talk, because—no matter how much you're drawn to the ideas in this book—your primitive brain guarantees a very short memory about why you're passing up that marshmallow.

If you were a "one marshmallow kid," beware of your inner rebel. You may be used to giving in to energy draining impulses that don't truly satisfy such as eating chocolate or sugary foods, drinking alcohol, masturbating, smoking, hot foreplay, or getting lost in TV or pulp novels. It's easy to mistake such gut-level cravings for your true will. Voluntarily adopting a daily recipe like the *Exchanges* is a way of countering the insidious hold of any self-destructive appetites. It's not too late to acquire the rewards of self-control.

"How Do I Know if Biology is Pulling My Strings...Again?"

Good intentions are not enough to divert you from the primitive pull toward fertilization-based sex. And it can be difficult to know when you're on the right track. Here are some clues that may help when you're in doubt:

Conventional Sex	Healing Sex
Impulsive, "spur of the moment" lovemaking	Gradual, conscious preparation prior to making love
Rapid movement	Emphasis on stillness
Tension	Relaxation
Urgent need for release	No need for release
Rapid conclusion	Prolonged union of cycles, erection comes and goes
Urgency to achieve a goal	Playfulness, ease in staying in the present, never hurried
Feelings of "I want," "I must have," or "hunger"	Can make love with enthusiasm, or defer without disappointment
Sex is just sex ("Get on, get off, get home")	Sex is a delicious experience of companionship and comfort
Sense that partner is trying to control you, "move too fast," or will abandon you	Sense of gratitude for time spent together. You feel very fortunate.
Avoidance of closer union—due to projection of sense of deprivation onto partner	Desire for closer union—due to projection of increasing sense of well-being onto partner

Happily, men who make up their minds to pass up orgasm achieve their goal fairly easily with a loving partner. Even if they have been ejaculating frequently, within a few days, their neurochemical "commands to come" quiet down. Perhaps it's because the hormone vasopressin, which appears to help them learn and remember why they want to wait for that second marshmallow, reaches ideal levels. That's the good news.

The bad news is that self-control during intercourse doesn't come as effortlessly to women. We, after all, are on the receiving end of things. Also, our open vulnerability actually assists our partner in controlling himself because it furnishes him with what he most needs from the encounter. As relationship expert, John Gray, put it, "A man is empowered and nurtured most when he feels appreciated, accepted and trusted....When a woman is longing to have sex with a man, she is most open and trusting. In a very dramatic way, she is willing to surrender her defenses...."[39] In keeping with our defenseless role, we apparently gush with cuddly oxytocin, and little vasopressin.

> ### Riddle
> Q: Why did the Irishman use two condoms?
> A: To be sure, to be sure

To be sure, most women do not start out as orgasm-prone during intercourse as men. Shere Hite (1976) found that only 30% of the women who responded to her questionnaire reached orgasm regularly from intercourse alone. However, using sex to heal seems to open us at deeper levels, so women grow increasingly sensitive and responsive. Since women are ideally in a more receptive role (energetically), this can spell trouble. For example, I have found that if my partner slides toward physical gratification I slide right with him, and soon come—with little or no warning. If his intentions are purely to nurture me safely, however, my control improves. In other words, his intentions are more critical to my maintaining balance than his actions.

The Key to Mortality

The point is that control is not the biggest challenge you face when you move toward a healing relationship. The biggest challenge is the millennia of distrust between the sexes caused by conventional sex. Deep in our collective unconscious, passion has a "bad rap." That is, tasty as that passion marshmallow is, it is also associated with subsequent chaos, emotional distress, and even spiritual demotion according to such diverse authorities as Adam & Eve and the Tibetan Buddhists.

Moreover, although we consciously associate passion with pleasure, another portion of our primitive brain views passion as suicidal. I believe this subconscious association accounts for the potency of the emotional rift between the sexes. Sex is the hub of the birth/death wheel. It brings us onto the planet and it is indirectly responsible for taking us off, too. It succeeds by gradually causing us to separate from each other, thus cutting ourselves off from our best source of rejuvenation.

The French refer to ejaculation as *la petite mort*, or the little death. If you ejaculate into your partner, the link between sex and this little death is projected onto her. Men who get the urge to bolt after sex aren't jerks ; they just can't face being chained to someone who's starting to look a little like a skull and crossbones "until death do us part." To be sure, running away merely cuts them off from the potential benefits of union, and guarantees them the same problem when their next "need for intimacy" (as relationship guru, John Gray, so delicately puts it) drives them into another encounter.

Not all of them run. Some, in obedience to this reflex of decline, begin to assure their deterioration through illness, addiction or impotence. This death reflex affects women, too. As one author put it:

> **The usual man or woman engages in sexuality through exclusive stimulation of the sexual center, not only losing the sexual chemistry but devitalizing the entire body-mind. [Conventional] sexual intercourse is thus a degenerative process.**[40]

Women also unconsciously create distance in relationships to stop this downward cycle. It doesn't matter how we do it: moodiness, hurt feelings, accusations, weight gain, irrational fears, illness, needing space, or growing in different directions. The bottom line is—we separate. In effect, the pursuit of genital orgasm seduces both sexes into running on short-life batteries instead of staying plugged into an inexhaustible source of strength and inspiration. And we don't even realize there's an alternative until we learn to sustain a heart link with a partner. That grows increasingly unlikely as we continue to hit this raw nerve of fear in our subconscious.

Look at *"Romeo and Juliet"* or *"The English Patient."* Our art, too, reflects this connection between passion and disaster. It's no wonder we often see the world as a place of decay and despair. Since I've become more observant of this connection between passion and death I've begun to notice how often a philosophy of gloom sets in during the weeks following a passion bout.

Not only do I experience uncharacteristic discouragement, men who normally exude energy, optimism and physical fitness will cynically explain to me that they don't want to live forever anyway to justify returning to a self-destructive habit or abandoning plans for personal growth they'd eagerly anticipated. A hangover from too much passion (or masturbation) even hits some of us in the form of severe depression and a desire to commit suicide, which we never consciously associate with sex. This despair is normal, but completely avoidable if we opt for an alternative approach to intimacy.

The reverse is also true. When making love without succumbing to passion, both I, and men who try the ideas, astonish ourselves with our productivity, insight, cheerfulness, sexiness, youthfulness and confidence. So I'm convinced we can evade this passion trap. For now, however, when genital orgasm creates feelings of dying a little, our body chemistry obediently responds by killing us a little. And this constant reminder of death seduces mankind into thoughts like: "we're all going to die anyway, so why not have a little pleasure first?" Indeed, perhaps you are beginning to see how conventional orgasm can lead us to bring about all the dire consequences eastern yogis warn of: weakness, lack of courage, and premature death. It's because of the uneasy body chemistry

71

that eventually follows the sensation of let down or emptiness after the high of orgasm.

Some men report a different experience. Rather than a let down, they often feel a frenzied euphoria after orgasm. The pursuit of orgasm may, in fact, cause them to seek dangerous thrills. The rush of PEA (stimulating stress hormone) that is so often present in initial sexual encounters, is also released in large quantities during the freefall of a parachute jump. Some researchers surmise that this rush may be addictive, perhaps due to the increase in dopamine that seems to accompany it.

In any case, I once read that the group who will most likely die accidental and violent deaths is men in their 20's. It's intriguing that a sort of "death wish" is most powerful when their sex drive is highest— and their inclination to stay with a partner long enough to awaken more beneficial ecstatic body chemistry lowest. (Higher testosterone levels during these years make both restlessness and the pursuit of sexual opportunities more probable.)

> ### Anthropological Clues
> According to an account in an English newspaper, the Hulis, aborigines of New Guinea, also known as "Wig Men,"
> > have a traditional distrust of women, believing that females take their powers from them. As a result they live apart from their bare-breasted wives and cook their own food. Sex is reduced to a brief encounter.
>
> Crude superstitions? Perhaps. Yet one Western, red-blooded, bachelor—who assured me he was typical—summarized his sexual routine as, "Get on, get off, get home." Incidentally, he has also learned to cook his own food since his divorce....Apparently some Wig Men aren't wearing wigs.

Maybe the Hulis aren't as eccentric as we suppose. At any rate, the real tragedy of the association between passion and death is that it does not get better over time. Each sexual encounter reawakens it—or the couple unconsciously avoids sex altogether to keep from triggering it, causing an unhealthy stagnation. If they stay together the relationship becomes an empty shell. I know of one couple who now see each other every three weeks or so. They call it "graceful distance." But all too often this subconscious uneasiness leaves us with a protective urge to grab the sex, but avoid the intimacy.

And that, folks, is how I came to discover the Key to Mortality: we each arrive here as a male or a female. And when we use (or disuse) sex in a way that does not promote harmony, the separation causes us to age more rapidly than we need to—or go out with a bang. So if you're currently scared to death of intimacy you aren't alone, but isn't it comforting to know that you're surrounded by millions of opportunities to reverse this unhealthy trajectory with a new approach?

> **I remember having been rather frightened as a boy when I first learned of examples in the animal world where the males die after having given away their sperm to procreate, e.g., the drones after the 'marriage flight' with the queen. What was so dangerous about marriage and sex?**   *Stephen*

"My Spouse Changed *Completely* After We Got Married"

You do not have to allow passion to create disquiet. You can reconfigure your neural reflexes relating to sexual intimacy by producing lots of cuddle hormones while avoiding passion entirely. That way you choose rejuvenation instead of activating all the fear-based "stuff" your subconscious associates with sex when passion is your objective.

You may still see some of your old defensive patterns for a while, but you'll see them with greater detachment than you ever thought possible. They won't have the same frightening subconscious charge behind them. And when you look back a few months down the road you'll find you've discarded them with remarkable ease.

73

Of course, the passion track remains in your brain, subject to reactivation. So if you stray back into passion, you will swiftly set off your old alarms—even if no one has an actual orgasm. Your partner will suddenly bear a striking resemblance to all your partners from failed past relationships (rolled into one decidedly scary looking creature). And your familiar, knee-jerk defenses to intimacy will kick in.

This occurs, you may recall, because a part of your limbic brain, the amygdala, has very efficiently recorded your past, unhappy emotional fallout from the pursuit of passion. It can't stop the impulsive sexual behavior mandated by other portions of the primitive brain (though you can—when you learn to resist that marshmallow), but it can do an excellent job of defending you from ongoing intimacy.

It regards *commitment* as the gravest threat related to intimacy because, when you commit, you tie yourself to a recurring sense of deprivation. Your amygdala therefore increases its alarm volume, creating stress (and distorted perception) in your relationship. I believe this perfectly understandable defense mechanism accounts for the familiar cry, "my spouse changed completely after we got married."

> "Honey, when we were together, you always said you'd die for me. Now that we're divorced, don't you think it's time you kept your promise?"   *Internet*

In over 10 years of watching myself and others, I never fail to be amazed at the efficacy of the amygdala. Its voice is loud and its advice is lousy. It is utterly single-minded, and its goal, once triggered, is to create separation between lovers, however it can, after we engage in conventional sex. As I mentioned earlier it, sends its red-alert messages out in the form of stress chemicals before we can even analyze its suggestions with our more evolved brain lobes. The effects linger, too. I notice the effects of a passion hangover for at least two weeks after a conventional orgasm. And it gets worse just before it gets significantly better.

This process of guarding us against deepening intimacy when we have engaged in passion is so mechanical and reliable that I call it the *Intimacy Sabotaging Device*. The only way I have found to escape its effects is not to pull its trigger. I make up my mind that my lover is regrettably not a marshmallow. He or she is in my arms to be healed. Period. Humanity has seldom used sex to heal, so our subconscious has no flashing danger signals related to such a foreign activity. And, humor aside, the benefits of giving are greater than those from receiving—as we saw in Chapter 3.

The Amygdala at Work
Yesterday Heidi, the woman I met on that bike tour, called me. We talked for about 2 hours. When she learned that my birthday is coming up she wanted to celebrate it with me. I felt 'attacked by surprise' and 'breathless.' I wanted to hammer her back—away from me. I told her I'd prefer to make a bike tour ALONE on my birthday. It's so subconscious. I didn't realize at first what I had done again.

There's always the feeling that if I engage too much in ANY relationship I will be imprisoned somehow and won't be able to be my own master, etc. How can I put my 'hammer' aside and learn to interact with people better? There's so much I want to give—but it always ends with me standing alone with empty hands...without having given anything.   *Gerhard*

What If One of Us Has a Conventional Orgasm While Trying This?

I sincerely hope I have motivated you to give the passion pit a wide berth. Yet this book would be incomplete if it didn't offer advice on coping with an activated Intimacy Sabotaging Device. If one of you has a conventional orgasm, whether awake or dreaming, first, mark the event on a calendar. That way you can watch the timing of the hangover for yourself and learn exactly how this strange separation virus works. You should be clear of the worst of the distress in about two and a half weeks if you don't reactivate your Intimacy Sabotaging Device.

Then, fasten your seat belts because you're in for a rough ride. Intimacy builds very rapidly with this healing approach—but the downside is that a hangover of disharmony is perceived as more painful than hangovers in the good ole days when you guarded your hearts more. Generally, by the time an accidental orgasm occurs during the *Exchanges*, your hearts are already opened and you've come to rely on a very high level of communication and trust between you. You will miss it terribly when it temporarily fades.

When your perception of each other shifts for the worse (and, again, watch out for that second week) it feels like it is permanent. Some word or action triggers an old pattern and suddenly you are both back on the relationship roller coaster. He may look incredibly selfish and self-centered. She may look unbelievably needy and demanding, or vice versa. And you literally can't feel the same ecstasy during sex.

The storm will pass but **there is no quick fix**. This cannot be repeated enough. You may hurt so much for a few days that you will be certain you have to do something drastic. Don't. The only place to solve your distress is where it began—preventing the error in the first place. And it's too late for that. Meanwhile, here are a few tips that can help with damage control.

- First, sleep together every night—even if you can't sleep, and even if every instinct in your body is telling you that you need your space. Recognize that the voice screaming in your head is just your Intimacy Sabotaging Device trying to do its job by destroying a potentially precious relationship (again). Ignore its commands as best you can.

- Second, promise each other you will not make any plans about the future of your relationship until two and a half weeks after the orgasm. Trying to resolve things while your perception of each other is skewed is most unwise. No matter how objective you try to be, you are drawing false conclusions based on exaggerated impressions. You are sure to see things differently when the hangover has passed.

If the silence between you gets too icy, you may each have to talk about your hallucinations, but try to preface your remarks with, "I know I'm going to see this differently in a few days, but..."

- Third, even though you don't feel up to it, do little things for each other without expecting anything in return, and without demonstrating your moral superiority by announcing what you've done. Selfless service will keep some giving and appreciation energy flowing between you. This counteracts the natural post-orgasm tendency to contract, judge harshly, or behave selfishly, by helping to open your hearts again and improve your body chemistry.

- Fourth, suggest you lie down and hold each other in silence as often as possible—even when it is not your turn to make a peace gesture. This is perhaps the single most powerful healing step you can take—though the benefits may not be instantly apparent. Please, don't try to talk it out until after an extended period of simply holding each other in silence or sleeping on it.

- Should a crisis come up, it may be wise to take a few *hours* apart from each other to regain composure.

- Should anger arise, acknowledge it and release it privately, or with a specialist, as soon as possible. Your lover should not attempt to be your therapist even if that his or her profession. Don't tax the safety and comfort of your relationship with this potentially explosive emotion. Anger is a natural symptom of the disease of life on a planet where we've all been uncomfortably off balance with no idea how to restore wholeness, but don't overestimate its staying power.

- It's wise to put your underwear back on and avoid intercourse for the period of the hangover. Treat your encounters strictly as healing meditations—and accept that, for a while, you will not feel most of the joy in each other's arms that you have been feeling. It will return in a couple of weeks. Meanwhile, take care not to indulge in passionate maneuvers in an attempt to substitute *heat* for *heart*.

- Decide that you'd rather be happy than right. That is, whenever you feel the least thawing between you, be ready to let go of your self-righteous conclusions—at least for long enough to comfort your lover. You'll feel better instantly.

- Finally, though it may sound paradoxical, wait until you're feeling good before you decide if you will break up. Otherwise you may soon be kicking yourself for giving up while under the influence of a temporary desire for separation brought on by a dopamine blast.

> Learn from others' mistakes....You may not live long enough to make them all yourself. *Unknown*

Be gentle with yourselves. You are trying something that is very new for you. Ultimately, persistence will triumph—but only if you stay together. And show some stamina because, once you derail into passion, it can be months before you stabilize the energy between you again. One passion error tends to bring about another during the two weeks following because it impairs judgment. During this rocky period the relationship may genuinely look hopeless at times. You may see temper tantrums, severe depressions, and old addictions take on new life.

One of my partners would lose all faith in himself and insist that I "should find someone with more self-discipline" because he just wasn't "strong enough." As it turned out, we were both soon the best partners either of us had ever had, but—thanks to our innocent errors—it took about 4 months before we really began to gain our balance. And even months later, old patterns of separation still occasionally arose (and were healed, as we learned not to identify with them).

Also, remember that as soon as you fall back into conventional sex you are dealing with an addictive behavior. A passion episode lights up your old neural pathways for sexual stimulation and reward seeking. Then when you try to go back on the wagon, it feels like your best friend (the Sure Dopamine Blast) has died, and you'll never REALLY feel good again if you can't get your passion fix. At a gut level your choice seems to be addictive bliss or boredom, pointlessness, and despair. Be tolerant of these perfectly natural symptoms. Do your best to make each other feel comfortable and loved as a dear friend no matter what happens.

Also, recognize that separation can strike your relationship in different ways during the fallout period. It does not always show up as relationship disharmony. If you manage to keep your hearts open, you will likely see your underlying stress and sense of deprivation externalized elsewhere in your life. One or both of you gets ill, faces a bitter disappointment, has an accident, or gets treated unfairly in some way.

Difficult as it may be to accept, we are shaping our own experience of the world. The way we choose to use our sexual energy has a major impact upon it.

Chapter 6
The Spread of the Separation Virus

On a recent visit to Nuremberg, my German host insisted we brave the chilly July rain to look at "The Marriage Carousel," Jürgen Weber's fountain in the heart of the city. The fountain is a vivid look at the ups and downs of marriage inspired by a poem written some four hundred years ago by famous "Nürnberger," Hans Sachs. As you walk around the fountain you see a couple go from their honeymoon in a swan boat through various stages of disharmony. It concludes with a comic look at them still grappling with each other in hell. Here are selected lines from the poem, which paint a poignant picture:

> ...How often during out 33 years of married life
> Were sweet and sour flavors
> Mixed with happiness and suffering
> First up, then down....
> My wife is the heaven of my soul,
> But also often my pain and hell.
> She is my freedom and my choice,
> And often my prison and cause of nostalgia...
> My wife is often amenable and good;
> She is also often angry and furious.
> She is my bliss and my heavy load.
> She is my wound and my bandage.
> She is my heart's delight
> And she makes me old and gray.

Four hundred years later his sentiments still resonate, and certainly women could pen equally colorful lines about their men. True, we can now have casual sex without disgrace and leave each other when heartache strikes. Departure, however, usually buys us a ride on the same carousel with our next lover. Whatever was not working in intimate relationships in the poet's day still is not working.

In fact, as the sexual revolution frees up passion across the globe, emotional separation between couples is becoming an even more virulent force. Among other things, it is accelerating the breakdown of the insular family unit. For now, most of us blame the churning in relationships solely on other things, such as readily available birth control, women working or collecting child support, easier divorce procedures, and more lenient religious attitudes.

These changes, however, do not account for the *urge to separate* itself. They merely make it easier for couples to split apart (or never commit). Something is stirring up an inability to stay together—and it's affecting even the most staid households. Much of this book has been devoted to explaining the origins of this urge to separate, but you may yet believe—as I once did—that this separation virus infects only a few. Actually, it is widespread.

The Bermuda Triangle of Relationships

Not only did Charles and Di blow apart (despite unlimited checking accounts and an enviable real estate portfolio), even the best matches all too often find their way into a mysterious "Bermuda Triangle." Despite all efforts to stay on course, many healthy unions between partners who are wise and loving, who communicate well, and who are quite at ease with their sexuality, give way to a relentless force. I used to listen to the castaways—trying to understand the patterns behind their individual experiences. Gradually, however, I realized that something larger, and quite *impersonal*, is at work.

81

It can't be overcome with good communication or even superior compatibility because this pathology is somehow linked to sexual intimacy—which is obviously an integral part of any healthy union. As long time marriage counselor and author, Willard F. Harley, Jr., said in his new book, *Love Busters*:

> **I want to emphasize that** [the utter selfishness that so often splits couples up] **is normal in marriage. You might think you're married to a crazy person or you may think you're crazy....**[But] **I'm thoroughly convinced that it's marriage itself, or more specifically a romantic relationship, that makes communication so difficult. It's not the differences between men and women....**[Those I counsel] **have very little trouble resolving conflicts when not in romantic relationship."**[41]

After years of careful observation, I had reluctantly reached the same conclusion. Relationships with sex in them clearly suffered from a baffling fragility. I call it a "virus" because it subverts a healthy element of union (intimacy) and transforms it into a means of damaging the host relationship.

A Woman's Rule of Thumb: If it has tires or testicles, you're going to have trouble with it.

No matter how good she looks, some other guy is sick and tired of putting up with her shit.

The best way to a man's heart is to saw his breastplate open.

"Make love, not war." Hell, do both, get married!   *The Internet*

Once I realized that sexual intimacy was somehow at, or near, the root of the problem, I focused more and more attention on happy marriages. How were others managing to evade this insidious force? Yet the closer I examined the "successes," the more evidence I found of gaps in them. True, in the happiest marriages, the partners were somewhat content with the compromises they'd constructed. Yet, upon careful inspection, the separation between the lovers was still quite evident. Instead of exhibiting immunity to the separation virus, they established that the disease was more universal than I'd first imagined.

As I listened to couples, and reflected upon my own two marriages, I grudgingly found myself devising a simple tool for pinpointing where the separation lay in unions. I nicknamed it *The Bermuda Triangle of Relationships* because the separation can be spotted in one of three areas. Once conventional sex enters a relationship between committed, sexually compatible partners who sleep in the same place, separation creeps in. At least one of these three aspects of the relationship begins to disintegrate: (1) the sexual attraction between the partners fades, (2) they become unavailable to each other sexually even though there is still an attraction between them, or (3) the couple's monogamous commitment breaks (or cannot form). And without these three cornerstones, the relationship is usually badly crippled, even if it does not die.

Let's look at these three elements in more detail so you will be able to determine for yourself if a couple has, in fact, beaten the separation virus:

Sexual Attraction

Lack of sexual desire is the most common problem clients bring to sex therapists. I know of a couple so harmonious that they were the envy of their friends for years. Then they shocked everyone by divorcing—on the theory that something must be terribly wrong because they weren't ever having sex—though they still loved cuddling.

Where Did My Libido Go?
"I've had to quit making love with my husband entirely," confessed an English friend in a small study group I often attended while in Belgium. "I found it always set off days of inexplicable depression." Moved by her admission, a German

---

friend told us, "After sex I used to get up and go into the bathroom and sit on the tub and cry. I couldn't imagine what was wrong with me. I had a nice husband, two wonderful kids and all the money I needed." A third (Danish) was also virtually sexually estranged from her husband and *somewhat* comforted to know the others were sleeping in separate bedrooms from their spouses, too. All were attractive, otherwise compatibly married, and quite comfortable with bodywork, intimacy, and alternative therapies.

Yet all of them opted to "let sleeping husbands lie," rather than try a new approach to lovemaking. One made a brief experiment first. She asked her husband if he would make love without conventional orgasm. After months of weighing involuntary celibacy against "crazy ideas," he agreed. They tried it once, without the suggested gradual exchange of energy over the preceding weeks. "The next day," she told me, "we were like teens in love. We took a walk in the woods. He even lifted me over a fence that unexpectedly barred our way. We giggled the whole way back to the hotel."

The results, though encouraging, were short-lived. The next time they made love, he begged to ejaculate "because it was his birthday," and she acquiesced. Within days he seemed to age 10 years. "I just can't stand the thought of touching him," she confided. Years later, their unresolved emotional and sexual distance is still a bitter drain on both.

Of course, such decreases in libido are no mystery once you grasp that conventional sex causes us to associate loving contact with distress—subconsciously, or otherwise. Our Intimacy Sabotaging Device is just protecting us by causing us to separate.

Sexual Availability

The subtlest way partners separate is by becoming unavailable to each other sexually—even though there is still an obvious spark between them. The reasons for the separation often appear to be beyond their control. This gap may take the form of incompatible sleeping habits, professional needs to live in different locations, allergies, kids' demands, TV or reading addictions, illnesses, inexplicable fatigue, sexual dysfunction, obsession with activities one's mate does not share, spiritual aspirations, and so on.

The Separation Treadmill

I work **50 to 60 billable hours each week**. My career has to be my first priority...at least until I find out if I'm asked to become a partner in my firm. Meanwhile, I just don't have the time or energy to make love much. Between the long hours and my commute, I'm exhausted.

My wife and I usually have to go away on vacation to make love, and that isn't easy since she's also a professional. Besides, it seems like every time we plan a trip, some crisis at one of our offices makes it impossible to go—or one of the kids gets sick.

Alan

Substance abuse is another common way couples keep a distance sexually. With alcohol, or marijuana, many drift in a haze of pseudo-intimacy, but very little lovemaking, for years. From the outside their marriages may look quite compatible.

Commitment

This is the most overt way couples separate. The relationship falls apart, or the partners opt for an open marriage (which usually leads to *emotional* separation even if they stay together). We have already seen how the hangover from conventional sex weakens a monogamous commitment. When the perception shift hits, and your partner looks "crazy" or "selfish," anyone else looks better (the "grass is greener" syndrome).

How Could I Have *Done* That?

I lived with my boyfriend for quite a while before we got married in college. We were nuts about each other and very

[continued...]

> sexually active. The relationship was good for us both. In fact, our grades noticeably improved. Yet, shortly after we married he began to pull away from me sexually. He couldn't explain why, and I couldn't bear the pain of knowing something was clearly wrong between me and my closest companion, with no way to understand it or resolve it.
>
> I had an affair with a fellow student. That healed my wounded feelings, but it also made me feel horrible. I'd always prided myself on being honest and genuine and yet my actions were totally the opposite. But it seemed like losing that sense of closeness with my husband made me feel so desperate that I had very little choice.
>
> *Lynn*

Whether or not anyone cheats, emotional disharmony makes ongoing commitment problematic. Someone opts for the noble sounding ideal of "needing more personal space," or both decide they are "growing in different directions." Is this problem widespread? For every two marriages that will occur this year in the States, another will end in divorce.

> **Why Isn't *Monogamy* the Problem?**
> Most of us accept that our hearts open best in an exclusive relationship. Yet I visited a community in Germany whose founders viewed monogamy strictly as an outdated, artificial, economic arrangement between men and women. They condone simultaneous liaisons with partners as a welcome historical correction. Feelings of jealousy or resentment are taboo.
>
> For years they also held workshops to help people explore their sexuality fully and even set up an erotic academy. One told me that they halted that line of development when "too many people became ill after the workshops." Incidentally, the women of the community have an unusually high incidence of pelvic inflammatory disease. In recent years the community
> *[continued...]*

86

has taken a more spiritual path seeking inspiration that extends beyond historical logic. And the core members of the community have moved toward depth of intimate connection and away from casual quantity. Indeed a number of them are now monogamous by choice.

I enjoyed the sense of brother/sisterhood open intimacy engendered among community members but polyamory ("many lovers") appeared to be a dead-end except when it led to finding a monogamous relationship in which to explore deeper union. If you know your partner is as likely to sleep with someone else tomorrow as he/she is to be with you there is a level at which you don't surrender. You keep things friendly, affectionate and sexy perhaps, but you defend your heart a bit. Of course, "Intensity Junkies" are often drawn to such environments because intense experiences are possible and it is perfectly acceptable to drop each partner as your post-orgasmic hangovers catch up with you.

Committed Monogamy

Availability   **Sexual Attraction**

So this is my Bermuda Triangle. The next time you spot a happy relationship with conventional sex in it, put it to the test. Hold it up against this model. Ask questions to check for gaps in the relationship. If the couple is open and honest I doubt you'll find your test case is the exception to the rule. Relationships with conventional sex develop symptoms of separation in one of these three areas.

On the other hand, it is equally obvious that if you want a healing relationship you need each of these three solid footings. Just beware that these cornerstones are not strong enough to withstand the unfortunate behaviors that, even according to the experts, normally accompany sexual relationships. This is why—despite my initial resistance—I've gradually concluded that we have to avoid the separation virus altogether by making love differently. Otherwise it weakens our relationships—or causes them to mutate into disappointing compromises.

Fairytale Marriages Under the Microscope

Popular wisdom, too, has it that harmonious romantic relationships usually thrive for a honeymoon period of less than a year. To cope with this reality many of us adjust our expectations downward. With the help of trained professionals, we redefine "happy relationships" as relationships that stay together though they show significant degrees of stress, emotional separation and deadening compromise. We are advised to manage these "healthy" relationships with better communication, endless negotiation, or even gross manipulation. Yet we aren't addressing the virus that brings our honeymoons to an end and does us the most damage in the process.

A recent study, which confirmed the clout of the honeymoon syndrome and measured some of its effects on our well-being, was conducted at Ohio State University. In 2000, Dr. Kiecolt-Glaser released results from a survey of 90 newlywed couples that ran from 1988 through 1992. Only couples who seemed to have everything going for them (and no addictions or emotional disorders) participated. So fewer than five percent of the applicants were selected from more than 2200 couples. On average they were well-educated and enjoyed annual incomes of $43,000. Most had dated for about three years before they married and three out of five had lived together before marrying. "These were highly healthy people. They were blissful!" explained one of the researchers.

By the second year of the study, the newlyweds' marital satisfaction had dropped significantly. As Kiecolt-Glaser put it, "Declines in marital satisfaction appear to be a stable response to the first year or two of marriage."[42] By the end of the study a fifth of them had already divorced.

> ### Her Side of the Story:
> He was in an odd mood Monday night when we met at a bar for a drink. I'd spent the afternoon shopping and I thought it might have been my fault because I was a bit later than I promised, but he didn't say anything much about it. The conversation was very slow going so I thought we should go off somewhere more intimate so we could talk more privately. But at the restaurant he was STILL acting a bit funny. I tried to cheer him up and started to wonder whether it was me or something else. I asked him if it was me, and he said "no." But I wasn't really sure. So anyway, on the way back home, I said that I loved him deeply and he just put his arm around me. I didn't know what the hell that meant because he didn't say it back or anything. I wondered if he was going to leave me! At home I tried to get him to talk but just he got another beer and switched on the TV. Reluctantly, I said I was going to bed. Then after about 10 minutes, he joined me and to my surprise, we made love. But, he still seemed really distracted, so afterwards I wanted to confront him. Instead I cried myself to sleep. I just don't know what to do anymore. I mean, I really think he's seeing someone else.
>
> ### His Side of the Story: Sox lost. Got laid though.

The study had an interesting objective: measuring stress hormones related to marital conflict. During the initial tests the couples were asked to discuss an area of conflict in their marriage for half an hour. Blood samples were taken before and after. Sure enough, hostility had increased the levels of three stress hormones. Regardless of the couples' apparent harmony, these hormones were consistently and significantly elevated in those who later divorced—and remained elevated hours after the discussion of marital problems, even while they slept.

The "His" and "Hers" joke is also aligned with the findings from the study. The increase in level of stress hormones was greater in women and was a better predictor of divorce than conflict behavior (that is, aggression or negative attitude) during the couples' initial discussions. Notice "Her" irrational insecurities and fears, projections onto him of her distressed state of mind, unhealthy preoccupation with his perceptions, lack of punctuality and sense of lack (compulsive shopping). Also, notice "His" puzzling "flatness" of mood, inability to relate except on a physical, sexual level, communication blackout, alcohol consumption, and total insensitivity to his partner's state of mind.

These symptoms, which are universal enough to make the joke funny, just happen to be typical hangover symptoms following conventional sex. Women tend to become clingy and over-react when the hangover strikes, while men tend to withdraw into their caves and numb themselves with sports or substances.

And, as Kiecolt-Glaser said, "these data may underestimate the actual physiological impact of marital discord, since the couples...were generally quite happy. In other work from our lab we have found that stress can alter responses to vaccines and slow wound healing. Thus, chronically abrasive marital relationships could have important health consequences." Not surprisingly, a Swedish study found that marital stress worsens the prognosis for women with coronary heart disease (while work stress does not).[43] The separation virus is hardly innocuous.

Obviously, it's not marriage, but rather harmonious union that benefits us. And the wrenching experience of watching our relationships dissolve in mutual stress or emotional distance is bad for us. Another study found that even individuals who were currently married, but had been through a broken marriage, were at significantly higher mortality risk compared with consistently married individuals.[44] Perhaps despair sets in more easily for those who have already experienced this virus in their lives.

Is the Situation Getting Worse?

Recently I picked up a book whose two male psychologist authors had considered naming, "*Women Are from Earth, Men Are from Uranus*." In fact they named it, *"Let's Face It, Men Are @$$H%c$! What Women Can Do About It."*[45] It was full of brutal advice for coping with abusive men who control intimate relationships with tactics like knowing-it-all, emotional distance, perpetual teenage behavior, or seductiveness. And, no doubt, men could justify a book entitled, *"Let's Face It, Women Are Bit*#@$,"* given the verbal abuse and psychological torment we so often engage in while suffering the effects of primitive brain programming.

The authors admitted that their goal was not to heal relationships, because, based on their experience, "men do not want to change." Instead the authors recommended coping strategies that included burning dinner, parking your partner in, out-silencing him, spending more and more time away from home, and dumping the two-timing charmers. It was entertaining, but it would have been very depressing had my own experience not convinced me that even relationships with these "hopeless cases" rapidly show signs of good health when they employ a new approach to sex. Meanwhile, many people have, indeed, reached the point of desperation. A gap is widening between the sexes.

> My mom said the only reason men are alive is for lawn care and vehicle maintenance.   *Tim Allen*
>
> Instead of getting married again, I'm going to find a woman I don't like and give her a house.   *Lewis Grizzard*

It's not just an emotional gap either. A U.S. Census report for 1996 showed that, since 1970, the number of divorced people had more than quadrupled, and the number of people who had never married had more than doubled. These two groups, combined, accounted for 40% of all adults—up from 28% only 26 years earlier. In the last forty years the divorce rate has gone from 15% to 50%. In short, committed union is not faring well—though a lot of casual sex is going on. The States, for example, has one of the highest rates of sexually transmitted disease in the industrialized world.

Until recently, across the globe, church (or social sanction) and state kept a pretty tight lid on sexual expression. Marriages were often arranged. Divorce was first impossible and then heavily censored. Birth control was unavailable or prohibited. And unsanctioned relationships were strictly punished. All these features of life ensured that any emotional separation between partners was partly masked (by the fact that they had to continue to live together). But they also meant there was just plain less fooling around after the honeymoon period ended. That left relationships stagnant, but less volatile.

Still these rules served the purposes of church and state—institutions that often benefited from stable family units preoccupied with procreation. Even now, despite increasing resistance, the Catholic Church is gamely trying to multiply the faithful by encouraging procreation at every turn. And not long ago I came across this headline, "*Sri Lankans Urged to Multiply for War.*" The article reported that the Sri Lankan Government is urging people to abandon the *Small is Beautiful* birth control campaign and have larger families, to swell the ranks of the army and the clergy. For the same reason, Mussolini ordered the church bells rung in the middle of the night so Italians would wake up and make babies.

I'm glad the sexual revolution is helping us squirm free of the shortsighted grasp of such institutions and I believe the transformation we're witnessing offers great promise for the future. But at the moment things are undeniably ugly. The increased pursuit of sex for the sake of physical gratification makes messes: unplanned pregnancies, churning relationships, stressed single parents, addicts, miserable kids, and despair about intimacy.

The good news is that our circumstances are so painful that many of us may soon be open to a radically different approach to lovemaking. When we master it the benefits will outweigh the heartache it has cost us to motivate our leap to a new level.

> **Lament of A Great Lover**
> Q: I love her, and the last time we made love she had *four*
>   orgasms. Why would she *leave* me?
> A: There is unfortunately no right way to do the wrong
>   thing.

A New Point of View

One coming gift is the ease with which we can regain our faith in humanity and forgive our past partners as we learn to use sexual relationships to heal each other. It is highly therapeutic to realize that the relationship craziness and chaos we've endured had little to do with humanity's hopeless flaws, different planetary origins of the sexes, our personalities...or mental health. Instead we innocently made ourselves nuts trying to please ourselves, or each other, in bed.

Frankly, this realization already gives my past relationship tragedies a decidedly comic gloss. I now regard our genitals and their blind drive to duplicate us as a sort of cosmic joke—one we no longer need to fall for. Those of us who have behaved the worst while trying to figure out what the heck to do with our sexual energy may, in fact, now be poised to spring into the lead in the discovery true harmony. We're more motivated to transform than those who are stuck in a less acutely uncomfortable stagnation.

As I've started to think in larger terms I'm increasingly intrigued by the implications of our current sex habits. I wonder how many inmates could have avoided lives of crime, addiction or insanity simply by having a clearer understanding of how to manage their sexual energy. Perhaps many such people are just particularly sensitive to our unsuspected sexual hangover. I wonder whether puberty could become a less traumatic experience if we knew better how to guide our offspring into safe, healthy contact with the opposite sex...and themselves.

I've even started to suspect. that cultural stereotypes develop quite innocently depending upon the accepted role of sex in a given milieu.

I've noticed that sex positive cultures, like the West Indies or parts of California, tend toward a more playful, relaxed approach to life—and careless pregnancies, addiction and unrealistic thinking. In contrast, more sexually repressed cultures, like much of Western Europe and its New World descendants, tend toward emotional isolation, rigid, judgmental thinking—and a more responsible outlook.

I think it'll turn out that the unhealthy aspects of these extremes will naturally melt away as we replace our inner sense that "something is missing" with frequent, satisfying union and the inner balance it creates. German psychiatrist, Wilhelm Reich, argued that dammed up sexual energy caused all social and personal ills. I think he was onto something. But whereas he seemed to feel release of sexual energy was the solution, the clues I've seen point to the exchange of sexual energy, via the heart, as the key.

The energy does have to move for us to feel fulfilled, but it doesn't have to move in the form of a genital orgasm. Instead it can move in a relaxed, shared ecstasy that gives us a lasting sense of well-being. Reich, after all, was a cocaine addict who married three times, so his emphasis on orgasm may, in fact, have been hurting him even if it also un-blocked him at some level.

In any event, as appalling as humanity's current sexual intimacy labor pains are, I'm looking forward to what the future holds as we learn to navigate around this weak point in our design, and chart our courses away from the Bermuda Triangle of Relationships. Instead of lowering our standards for intimate relationships to align with the ravages of the separation virus, let's try raising them substantially—to the level of mutual healing. What have we got to lose?

Chapter 7
Crossed Wires

Woman: When I first ran into this idea that the alienation between men and women was a problem for everyone, I had only been with women. In fact the thought of a man touching me made me feel like unfriendly bugs were crawling on my skin. In any case, I had always been invisible to men except as a friend or colleague. So even after I began to make a conscious effort to heal my feelings toward men I figured this theory of union between male and female would remain theoretical for me.

Within a week, a male colleague asked me out. It took all my courage, but I went—because even though I was not at all attracted to him, I sensed there was a larger reason behind such a surprising event. I wasn't ready for a relationship with a man yet, but I was amazed by his sensitive acceptance of my past, and his obvious high regard for me. It was a healing experience.

While living in Europe I developed a close friendship with Mark, a gay American. We spoke almost every day on the phone and shared everything. He was the brother I'd never had. One day I asked him, "If there were a pill one could take to become straight, would you want to take it?" I was expecting him to say, "Certainly not, I love men." Instead he answered, "Yes, in a heartbeat." When I mentioned Mark's answer to another gay friend he said, "Of course. I would, too." And when I asked him why, he said, "because I have the sense that my wires are crossed."

Poof! There went my picture of happy homosexuals who were just like me except for a reverse spin on gender orientation. Of course, since those discussions, I've come to realize that we have even more in common than I'd initially imagined. Indeed, everyone on the planet has a case of crossed wires thanks to our primitive brains—they're just crossed in different ways and some are more colorful than others. From my revised vantage point there is little difference between promiscuous singles, confused priests, loving lesbians, heterosexuals stuck in emotionally distant marriages, adventurous bi-sexuals, lonely masturbators, or even blander variations on the theme of human sexuality. All are but indicators of a deteriorating dynamic of separation between the sexes. I'm confident that no one's attempt to cope is inherently, or morally, superior to any other. And none of them heals the dilemma I'm addressing either.

Who's Driving?

At the time, though, I was floored by these answers. An image of people trapped on a bus, with a crazed driver at the wheel, careening down a mountain to some destination they would never have chosen, haunted me. When I talked to a close lesbian friend about it she assured me that gay men were *different*. With an air that implied lesbianism represented the next rung of human evolution, she explained that she and her friends were *more* than satisfied with their lot.

I found that easy to believe. By then I'd been through the hamburger grinder of heterosexual relationships way too many times and the concept of a relationship with a close friend of the same sex struck me as eminently sensible. I wouldn't have to explain to her repeatedly how to make me come. I could "PMS" without feeling like a public nuisance. Indeed, I toyed with the idea that *I* was the unhappy prisoner—of the sensors in my nose that melt me in the presence of some sets of male pheromones.

Any thoughts of "reform" were dashed, though, when she showed up in tears to stay with me for ten days. Her lover was so addicted to orgasm that if Chris didn't make love to her every night Jen would "accidentally" hit her while she slept. This time the violence had erupted while they were awake. Chris was a battered woman.

With some regret I concluded that I might as well stick to men. Obtuse as they often were at least they never hit me. At the end of her stay I watched with horror as Chris returned to her unhealthy relationship. And

96

since I'd counseled her to leave Jen, she pretty much quit talking to me—
except to complain that the elegant Jen was gaining weight, which
apparently was not part of their unwritten contract. At any rate, when I
saw them a couple years later, they had both aged a lot, and begun to
smoke.

> The Bible contains six admonishments to homosexuals and 362
> admonishments to heterosexuals. That doesn't mean that God
> doesn't love heterosexuals. It's just that they need more
> supervision. *Lynn Lavner*

The Prince and the Frog

But back to Mark. Early on, our friendship was very challenging for me
because he sometimes engaged in unsafe sex in the bushes of a city park.
In the midst of an AIDS epidemic it was hard to sit with the fact that
someone I dearly loved was trying to destroy himself. But I accepted
that I "was not his mom," so—except for paying for his clinic visit to
treat a case of gonorrhea—I remained in the role of confidant. To be
sure, I also showered him with lots of advice about the hidden perils of
genital orgasm, and we talked frequently about intimate details.

Mark shared that he masturbated relatively infrequently—as compared
with another gay friend who'd transformed his second bedroom into an
altar to pornography. But whenever he did, it was soon followed by a
devastating loss of self-confidence. Some event, like a discussion with
his family—who were not thrilled about his bumming around Europe
without a career—would unnerve him completely. And that's when he'd
go off to the bushes feeling worthless.

It took some time to spot the pattern but he finally quit masturbating.
Not only did he then forsake the park shrubbery, but within a few months
he got together with one of his early lovers in New York City, whom
he'd lost contact with ten years earlier. Theirs became Mark's first real
relationship ever. That was definite progress, though they did sometimes
have conventional orgasm—despite my evangelism. Things were

predictably chaotic, too, and they screamed at each other a lot. Mark was an accomplished mooch and Eric, an interior architect, understandably frequently lost his patience with being manipulated.

About a year into their relationship I moved to New York City. Eric had just given Mark a tyrannical ultimatum so Mark and I decided to apply for jobs at a soon-to-open Barnes & Noble superstore. We started work at a time when Mark and "Mr. Wonderful" (as Mark called Eric) were estranged. Eric was out of town and Mark was working up the courage to leave him—now that he had a job. I stayed at their place because he wanted company and we hung out, laughing and talking, for several weeks.

During those weeks I got a glimpse of a very different Mark. Our employer had a clever strategy for appointing managers. It threw all 450 employees into a 4 story building together as equals. Boxes had to be unloaded, moved around, and unpacked, so teams spontaneously formed, and leaders appeared. I was dazzled as Mark bloomed into a brilliant natural leader: charismatic, hardworking, funny, reliable, and a genius at kidding slackers into full participation (after all, who knew more than he did about evading work?).

He also crackled with a magnetic, thoroughly masculine, electricity I'd rarely glimpsed, but which he now wore as naturally as a fairytale prince. He flirted with women in ways that melted us all, and everyone of both sexes wanted to work with him. It came as little surprise that he was promoted twice in those first two weeks.

> When you love somebody, your eyelashes go up and down, and little stars come out of you. *Karen, age 7*

Unfortunately he was soon to slip back into his frog costume. The last day before Eric's return, he helped me carry my stuff back to my cramped apartment, and we had a long talk about his relationship blues. I invited him to share my space until he, or we, could find another place to live. He was torn. He was acutely aware that before him was an open gate to a totally different lifestyle but it was also scary. When he left he went straight to a Times Square porn theater and jerked off.

His queeny persona swiftly reappeared. He decided to stay with Mr. Wonderful, "because his apartment was so much nicer." He began to offend people at work with his manipulative gossiping and it wasn't long before he quit his job at the bookstore. As he explained, "Eric needs me to help him select *fabric* samples and I just *love* fabrics!" I couldn't help wondering just how many of the world's great natural leaders are confining their talents to fabric selection.

> **I was celibate while I attended a six-month training program in California. When it ended I decided to travel before returning to Amsterdam. One of my first stops was a gay beach where I had sex. I was amazed at the depth of the depression that followed within days. It made me think back to the times when I visited such beaches regularly in Holland. I was always sick. Maybe some people aren't affected by it, but sex the way I've been using it does create a hangover for me.**
>
> **My path of personal growth has been to acknowledge my true worth and deepest desires. As I've moved toward what I really want my diet has changed to healthy food, my job has changed to activities I enjoy, and I am ready to try this approach to sex. Deep inside I know sex was not created to make me feel bad afterward, but to allow me to create union between people regardless of their gender.** *Joshua*

The Penny Drops

Six months later I, too, left Barnes & Noble to take a job as Cabaret Room Manager for a gay nightclub in Greenwich Village. For almost a year, I designed posters for drag queens, made many homosexual friends, and talked with people about humanity's separation virus. Initially I was amazed at the open-mindedness of my homosexual friends. Then it dawned on me that people drawn to same sex relationships have probably spent more time wondering about the reasons for alienation between the sexes than anyone...but me. Far from being threatened by my ideas, many related easily. In fact, almost all friction surrounding my thoughts about same sex relationships has come from well-meaning, but overeager, heterosexual defenders of diversity. Diversity's a nice objective, but if you're trapped on a bus you wouldn't have chosen to board in the first place, it may not be your chief concern.

Anyway, a couple years later, a mutual friend (whom I hadn't known was bi-sexual) introduced me to Kate. My friend, who enjoyed drama, had "forgotten" to tell me Kate was homosexual. "On a 1-10 scale of lesbianism, I'm about a 15," Kate told me later. "I've never slept with a man. I can't even stand the *thought* of it. I *love* women, though." However, that evening I missed the signals: the discreet rainbow earring, the black leather jacket, and the defiant glint.

I only saw a brilliant engineer with a remarkable ability to concentrate, a broad-ranging background in spiritual matters, and a powerful will—who asked some of the best questions I'd heard. Thus began a lively exchange between two very determined Truth Seekers. We agreed on a surprising number of major points—including the concept that the split between male and female is the means by which humanity perpetuates its dualistic thinking. She did not, however, accept that curing an unwholeness of *mind* might call for *physical* union with the other half of our species as a starting point.

"But what if unconditional giving, even to that extreme degree of nurturing, were necessary?" I theorized. "Could you agree to reunite with a man in the role of a planetary healer?" She was studying for an additional degree in naturopathy by correspondence and people often came to her for advice. "You wouldn't say you could only treat women, if a man needed help, right?"

"Of course not. I help anyone. I just *enjoy* helping women a lot more," she smirked. I countered, "I think your discrimination goes deeper than you think. You forgive women anything while you become completely exasperated with a man who does something you don't like."

She got very quiet. "I'll work on it," she said with the grim determination of a true spiritual warrior. A week later, I got an Email from one shocked lesbian! Following her deep spiritual work on releasing resentments she was harboring toward men, a male colleague asked her out. The day of their date she suffered a horrible migraine, but the evening was quite a surprise. She ended up telling him all about herself. He only wanted to know if there might be a future. There wasn't. She was about to take a job in another state. But several myths had exploded before her eyes. She'd realized she did need to heal her feelings toward men. And that as she did she was no longer invisible...for better or worse.

Uh oh...

To be sure, Kate still had powerful desires to hang out at lesbian bars and websites. But she decided to follow her inner guidance and grudgingly opted for "neutral"—just temporarily, you understand. She let her hair grow a bit and didn't announce her sexual preference at her new job.

A few months later something had definitely shifted. Men, whom she had previously viewed as thick-witted obstructionists, now fell over themselves opening doors, grinning, offering help, furniture, and information. "And when I wear a skirt they say, 'Good Morning' to my legs," she laughed. "Of course, I like women's legs, too...." When I next saw her she was a different woman. A welcoming smile lit her face where before there'd been a defensive impassivity. She laughed more often. She no longer gave off an air of *Kate Against the World*.

She began to hang out with a male colleague with whom she shared a lot of sporting and technical interests. There was no passion or sex, though. "Justin has never even tried to unbutton my shirt," she informed me (smugly). I was puzzled because he sure spent a lot of time with her. Finally she admitted she'd begun masturbating again months earlier. (Shortly after we became friends she'd told me that, on orders of her inner guidance, she'd given it up during the month before we met—

which may have given her the clarity and courage to listen to ideas she would normally have blown off.)

With masturbation back in the picture the lack of sparks between Justin and her was totally comprehensible. As explained in Chapter 2, masturbation depletes sexual magnetism though it increases the desire for more orgasm. And it sends out an unspoken message of, "I don't need you. I can take care of my sexuality myself." I encouraged her to give it a rest just to test the theory. She struggled for months—perhaps because it was a defense. Finally one of her best friends came to visit for three weeks, which gave her the support she needed to let it go.

As soon as her friend left, Justin began kissing her passionately, and, to her surprise, she even enjoyed it. One thing led to another. Then she let him make love to her "just to see if she could do it without feeling sick." She was so bent on her experiment that she ignored all my advice about approaching intercourse slowly and consciously and avoiding orgasm. She didn't even ask him to control himself. "I would have enjoyed a pizza a lot more," she told me after the Big Event, "but at least I didn't freak."

About four days later, however, he had a sudden stomach flu, and a few days after that a panic attack while kayaking with her. She was dismayed by his sudden weakness, which endangered both him and the guide who had to rescue him. The following weekend she accepted a date to go hiking with another male colleague. Justin was furious. She was self-righteous. They swiftly grew apart. Shortly thereafter she moved in with the hiker with whom she still lives. Her career has taken off, and I'd like to be able to say that everything is going great between them, but it isn't. They've made no effort to avoid conventional sex, and now they hardly ever make love, much to her disgust. She's gone back to masturbating—and fantasizing about women.

Moral of these stories? Forgiveness and avoiding masturbation, while hanging out with a member of the opposite sex, are the keys to uncrossing your wires (that is, the secret to spontaneous enthusiasm for intimate contact with the opposite sex). Yet going straight is not the key to relationship harmony—you need to make love differently. I know she'll work it all out in her own time. And thanks to her and Mark I will never again believe the current alienation between male and female is irreversible—even if our chosen defense is sexual preference.

> Sex is one of the nine reasons for reincarnation. The other eight are unimportant. *Henry Miller*

Mystery Revealed?

Of the homosexual friends I've mentioned so far, one is a gifted pianist and conductor, one is a technical genius and a remarkable athlete, and three are fluent in three languages and also excellent musicians. Most have unusually heightened spiritual perception (active third eyes). Unfortunately, all these talents matter little because they cannot make the most of their abilities. The pianist, for example, could be a great composer—if he would find another use for his second bedroom. The engineer is like a meteor, in serious danger of burning out from overload (imbalance), and suffering from severe endometriosis (a condition that often necessitates hysterectomy).

And the signals from their enhanced spiritual vision, though often loud and clear, are usually disregarded in the inner storms their urges brew up. This causes severe bouts of self-hatred because their intrinsic standards are high, but, in their judgment, their behavior is often outrageous. In short, they experience an extreme version of what all of us go through while our primitive brains rule.

So when I stumbled upon the following explanation in an esoteric book,[46] it rang true. Unlikely as it may appear, extraordinary abilities, vivid imaginations, and frequent masturbation beginning early in life (a trait they also shared) may all be linked to lofty, but sexist, spiritual aspirations in a past life. Here's how.

103

It's well-known in esoteric circles that it is possible to expand our spiritual vision, even without a partner, by re-channeling our sexual energy upward with rigorous self-discipline. Some of us have taken this radical step of forcing open our third eye in past lives. To do it, we chose to cut ourselves off from the opposite sex entirely. (And, given the fallout from conventional sex, we may have welcomed celibacy by that point.)

With our newfound power we not only expanded our awareness but also cultivated exceptional mental, artistic, healing, psychic or other powers. We could never have developed them had we continued to stagnate in the standard marriage / conventional sex / procreation / support-the-offspring cycle that entraps most of humanity.

Yet this course of action had a hidden drawback. When we strengthen ourselves psychically in one lifetime we start our next lifetime with an unusually strong flow of life force energy. All this power proves extremely destabilizing, for we arrive with enhanced imaginations, hypersensitivity, and more sexual energy than most—but no instruction manual.

And, of course, we are still not inclined to nurture a member of the opposite sex. After all, we forced our past progress precisely by avoiding them, rather than healing them. When we hit puberty, these factors (loads of sexual energy, ignorance of why and how to manage it, distain for the opposite sex, and fertile imaginations) often combine to addict us to masturbation.

Frequent masturbation, however, causes disequilibrium, which increases paranoia and a sense of alienation from anyone onto whom we project it. This makes us feel different from others on many levels. Indeed, as Gay Pride Day always colorfully demonstrates, terminal uniqueness reigns supreme in the homosexual community. If we choose a lifestyle that encourages frequent orgasm our sense of being different virtually entraps us. Voila! We're now prisoners on a bus we might well not have boarded had we been able to remember the true significance of, and loftier options for, our sexual energy. This phenomenon of feeling odd as the result of frequent masturbation also affects straight—and undecided—people.

> *Man, 60*: I was sure I was bi-sexual all these years. But the results from circulating my sexual energy instead of masturbating have been so dramatic (a sense of direction, an open heart, a desire to connect with others, a new joy in music) that I'm open to another approach. I want to see for myself what this kind of union with a woman can do.

Heart/Genital Splits

Most of this book is about the gap that develops between the *hearts* of heterosexuals who've joined genitals. So I'm lumping spiritual celibates into this chapter on same sex relationships because they, too, show the reverse pattern of alienation from the opposite sex. That is, they deliberately separate at a *genital* level.

Having visited four spiritual communities in three countries, I have a number of celibate, and aspiring-to-be-celibate, friends. And after years of listening and observing I'm convinced that some celibates so dearly love members of the opposite sex (as a part of their love for humanity), and are by nature so gentle, that they simply can't face the ugly fallout from conventional sex. They are frightened of sex—with good reason.

Perhaps they've had to dry the tears of an abandoned parent or watched someone turn abusive under the influence of the separation virus. They sense (or have experienced) that they, too, could do something hurtful if they engaged in conventional sex—and so they don't. They give their love to God, the earth, or other causes, and they comfort themselves with good deeds, prayer, meditation, medication or recreational drugs. They are, of course, perfectly positioned to establish sexual relationships that heal once they realize there is a nontoxic approach to intimacy.

I also believe some homosexuals seek to avoid hurting the opposite sex by selecting a same sex partner. Same sex relationships initially feel more comfortable because those of the same gender tend to deal with post-orgasm fallout the same way. It's easier to cope with a sexual hangover, if both of you process things to death, or both of you withdraw emotionally.

Though they park their genitals elsewhere members of these two groups often make deeper heart connections with the opposite sex than most heterosexuals ever attain. That is, ardent heterosexuals who copulate willingly, but can't create a genuine emotional tie with a partner, are no closer to uncovering the mystery of a healing synergy between the sexes than those who keep a genital distance. Yet a split between heart and genitals, whether it's north or south of the waistline, is still a symptom of mankind's separation virus.

New Hope for Fetishists
Another way we suffer from crossed wires is through sexual fetishes. Sexual arousal, of course, can innocently become associated with truly bizarre things. Yet for those afflicted it's no laughing matter. A close friend discovered in her late thirties that the torture fantasies that ran in her head whenever she was trying to climax were the product of some insignificant (but apparently painful) genital snipping her pediatrician did when she was a baby. Discovering the cause didn't heal the association, however. In fact, she still never came without heart-closing, torture movies running in her head.

Happily, when she began using this approach to lovemaking, the fantasies swiftly receded, never to return. Placing her attention on her partner's well-being instead of her own orgasm was the cure. Most fetishes are linked to orgasm. As long as that payoff is in view it is very hard to let them go. Once orgasm is no longer the goal, however, they lose their addictive grip.

Spiritual Celibacy

My friends aspiring to religious celibacy proved far less open minded about the existence of a separation virus than my homosexual pals. After all, ancient religious traditions abound that revere sexual avoidance of the opposite gender. In fact, those who view sexual desire as a weakness—which is easy enough to do on this planet—give extra points to yogis, monks, nuns, and themselves when they are successfully celibate. So they generally disparaged my suggestion that acetic traditions might have overlooked the peace of mind attainable through another approach to union.

Their intransigence surprised me because celibate traditions clearly affirm the correlation between inner peace and a combination of unconditional love and abstinence from orgasm. So I'd figured those with serious spiritual practices would be among the first adherents to this ancient approach—especially in light of the many scandals surrounding gurus and clerics. Clearly, we haven't found a reliable path to spiritual enlightenment unless it incorporates sexual desire.

Instead, I was surprised to find that when they broke their vows, they did so with abandon. They resisted taking a slow approach to sex and tended to focus on their own sexual gratification. After binging, they swiftly returned to their special relationship with God, or the feet of their chosen spiritual master. They'd explain, often with distain for anyone who didn't share their need to atone, that it was an error to think sex could be anything but a red herring for one on a spiritual path. Then, at their next opportunity, they'd do it all again—often with a noticeable lack of regard for the partners they used. They even found it difficult to treat their "errors" with compassion, perhaps due to guilt projections. At any rate, the concepts of *sex that is not oriented toward physical gratification* and *selflessness toward an intimate partner* eluded them.

The friends for whom the bell really went off in response to my hypothesis were those with intense spiritual practices, who had also tried celibacy, yet generally opted for relationship. They've quickly grasped that sex without orgasm is the obvious way to be in integrity with your spiritual work and at peace with your sexuality.

So if celibacy has not lived up to its promise of peace of mind and a seat at God's right hand, stop fighting yourself, and try a more generous approach to a higher end. Remember, if you insist on climbing the mountain alone, your gains may be of little value next time around because your inner balance is not complete. Indeed, unless you have healed all subconscious alienation from the opposite sex and your love is unconditional, you may unwittingly be reserving both a seat on the "hopelessly-driven-by-my-impulses" bus and a costume of the gender you are avoiding (so that you can master compassion for its challenges).

Be Bold

From what I've seen of the damage inflicted by our primitive brains, no attempt to cope is surprising. Many of us have understandably unzipped the zipper between male and female completely in response to our uneasiness. Yet we may have the option of healing the unconscious impetus *behind* that choice.

So if you're settling for an uncomfortable ride, on a bus you're not driving, to a destination you wouldn't have chosen (or if you just can't get your bus up the mountain on your own), you may have an unsuspected alternative. You may be able to re-pattern your subconscious by gently *un*doing the past damage your procreation-based programming mindlessly caused. Whether you're now gay, celibate, straight or undecided, the damage takes the form of a protective urge toward separation from the opposite sex (at some level). Therefore safe, healing union *between* the sexes most directly replaces the old programming—restoring your free will and offering a fresh start.

The first phase of the *Exchanges* does not include intercourse. So if you try them, you'll have plenty of time to assess whether or not you do indeed feel a new sense of ease and wholeness—before intercourse is even an option. Think about it. It could put you in the driver's seat.

Chapter 8
Will My Partner Go for this Idea?

Three People on an Airplane

Woman passenger: Last night I saw a TV program about sexual issues called, "Strictly Personal." The topic was, "Men Who Fake Orgasm." This attractive guy in his mid 30's was explaining that he really enjoys making love, but he doesn't always want to come. The problem is that his girlfriend thinks there's something wrong with *her* if he doesn't come. So he shared how he uses condoms when they make love, fakes the orgasm, and then quickly disposes of the condom.

Italian-American construction worker in his early thirties: Ha, ha, ha…Men who fake orgasm! That's the funniest thing I ever heard.

His best buddy, also an Italian-American construction worker: I've done that.

Who tries this other approach to sex? You might be surprised. This chapter is a collection of people's stories about why this approach to sex makes sense to them.

I found this on my Email not long ago from a male acquaintance (age 35) in the UK:

I can tell you first-hand that the approach to ecstatic union works. What I didn't tell you when you were here is that I've practiced that approach out of personal choice/personal discovery for more than five years now. It is a better way. Your material did me the enormous service of identifying the dynamics of disempowerment that accompany the regimen of explosion.

And this account was so poignant that I decided to include it all:

109

Before I had a clue what sex was I knew I wanted to be in love. At age 7, I had a wonderful "love affair." It was divine. It was pure. It was innocent—and completely heart chakra. Amy Willis and I adored each other. When she moved in third grade I knew I wanted another relationship like that. I was sad she left but still an optimist. I didn't know it was going to be all down hill from there. I've always had a strong attraction to the opposite sex, but I have to admit that after the act of sex entered the picture, love was a lot more complicated.

Thanks to internment in an all boys prep school I remained fairly naïve until college. There I faced a most traumatic sexual experience: pregnancy and an abortion. Sex was a wonderful, natural by-product of being in love with someone, but my body clearly wanted to make babies every time I engaged in it. So for that reason and because I was really looking for a lover, not merely a "sexer," I was less apt to engage in casual sex than some of my classmates of the pre-AIDS sexy seventies.

I was a slow learner about some of the facts of life, though. Sex, for me, was the ultimate act of union so a piece of latex between my lover and me seemed like a major desensitizing compromise. Whenever I had a lover we tried to time our efforts with her cycle or I would withdraw before ejaculating. Although I was not especially promiscuous during the seventies and eighties I was responsible for more abortions—which caused a lot of heartache for all concerned.

I began to grasp that although there was a lot of pleasure connected with sex—which God must have intended us to have—the planet was painfully over-crowded. And there I was, responsible for a bunch of unwanted pregnancies. I could see it would be a great idea to find states of ecstasy without ejaculating into the woman, but early on I didn't make much progress. As the Beatles put it the goal was to *Come Together.*

Finally—after the most tempestuous (read: "passionate") relationship of my life *and* a set of twins—I was convinced that ejaculating into a partner had definite drawbacks. In the nineties, I began to experiment with avoiding orgasm during intercourse. Ironically, this was made easier because, with the advent of deadly communicable diseases, I was at last wearing condoms.

I still wanted the magical, mystical union of love and I still wanted to please my partner. And my partners still wanted to come during intercourse. Of course, I thought I was a very good lover because due to my increasing control they came...over and over and over. No longer self-indulgent I'd become a "pleaser." The big turn on was her excitement. It's really how I'm received that lights me up. If my lover received me with ecstatic enthusiasm the pleasure just built and built. And no one got pregnant!

Still, if my lover was coming all over me repeatedly all night long, and I wasn't coming at all, an emotional gap ensued. I might add that blow jobs always felt weird to me ... I don't want to be serviced; I want to be in some sort of mutual bliss. I've always liked to line up my chakras with my lover's—not have my lover somewhere else, like two feet below my chin.

So to pull this rambling to an end, when I read your material suggesting that the way we're using sex links love with fear and results in disharmony, I had to admit that all my relationships had ended in separation. It didn't matter whether I came, or we both came, or only she came. The one possibility I hadn't even thought of, let alone tried, was both of us *not* coming.

Truth is, I've always wanted a soul mate and yet my deepest relationships have not been very healing because there *is* a battle of the sexes going on here. It's kinda cute in a Katherine Hepburn/Spencer Tracy movie, but in my life it's only been painful. In fact, I think the separation of/battle between male and female is the most tragic thing happening on the planet.

111

I'm a "flaming" heterosexual and, in spite of the love I feel for my brothers, I want to merge with a <u>woman</u>. I'm plenty male myself, and it feels like I need the balance of yin energy to complete some...circuit. I mean I feel like a whole man, but that's only half of the equation. Disharmony between the sexes prevents the union I'm longing for. So if sex as conventionally practiced is, indeed, leading to such pathetic results, I figure there must be another way, or ...it's all just hopelessly screwed up. All I know is there is something tantalizing about the possibility of this last unexplored option being the key to getting off the roller coaster.

A Man's Guide to Female English [Further Studies]
- If she says, "It's your decision" it actually means "The correct decision should be obvious by now"
- "We need" means "I want."
- "Do what you want" means "You'll pay for this later"
- "You have to learn to communicate" means "Just agree with me"
- "We need to talk" means "I need to complain"

The Internet

Here's an account of another explorer:

I'd always been very sexually active, and for years I'd been fascinated by the idea of cultivating sexual energy for a higher end. For a long time, though, I thought *intensity* was the goal. In fact, twenty years ago I had my first demonstration of the power of an intense spiritual connection with a woman I eventually married. For three months I nurtured a connection with her. We didn't have intercourse during those months because we were housed with a group while we learned rebirthing therapy. Yet we enjoyed a sense of spiritual connection that far surpassed what I'd previously experienced in sexual union.

After the training, I returned home, and not long afterward, I made love with an old girlfriend. There was an immense pre-orgasmic high followed by a profound experience of energy depletion. It was as though an inner balloon of light energy filled with love burst and released into her leaving me instantly drained—as though I were only a body with little life force energy to sustain it. I just wanted to sleep because there was no energy to stay awake. It wasn't a simple refractory period. I lost a profound sense of heightened spiritual awareness because of a very localized, fleeting pleasure.

Then I married the first woman convinced that our spiritual connection could withstand anything. It couldn't. I watched our six-year marriage disintegrate into the most painful experience of my life. Ten years after the divorce I was still shattered from our protracted, bitter parting. I'd transformed from a very sexual man into an ascetic who just didn't "do relationship" anymore. Now that I've read this material I wonder whether all that happened because we were compatible, skilled lovers and simultaneous orgasm was a regular feature of our sex life.

This next man is large, and has still found a way to make love comfortably for hours:

I've always been in the vanguard of sexual exploration. I was a sannyasin (devotee of Osho) for years. Now I manufacture "yab yum benches" (for making love while sitting face to face) and "love swings." The swings allow couples to make love for hours with very little effort (he stands, she reclines). The swing has been a great teacher. The first time I tried my own invention I was frustrated because, though the lovemaking was great for us both, I couldn't ejaculate! For an hour and a half I kept asking my partner to get on the bed so I could come. She wouldn't.

Then something totally unexpected happened between us. For the first time I experienced what I call, "the realm of true pleasure." It wasn't the tension-release I'd previously defined as pleasure. Looking into her eyes during our prolonged union I "went somewhere else" altogether. And it was wonderful.

113

I've tried to sell the product to tantra types but often they're bent on consciously suppressing and forcing their sexual energy rather than welcoming such a simple solution. My product yields powerful results precisely because it doesn't permit stress. The lovers stay relaxed instead of tensing up.

> What do I know about sex? I'm a married man. *Tom Clancy*

What About Women?

Here are some of the reasons women switched to a non-orgasmic approach:

I had very mixed feelings about trying sex without orgasm. First of all it's not easy for me to avoid it. Multiple orgasms have always come easily for me. Also, I have been taught to please men even when they make unsound choices. Then, too, I didn't want to be thought peculiar for suggesting such a novel idea. Eventually, however, the chaos in my love life made me vow to give it a try. The results, while mixed, have convinced me that this *is* the solution. Now I just need a cooperative partner. Here's what happened:

When I met Costas, a Greek naval officer, he was charming, jovial and full of energy. We talked for hours about The Meaning of Life, as Greeks regard themselves as the only true great philosophers. He also taught my friends and me Greek dancing. When we became lovers, though, we continued to go round and round. He would make love without orgasm and be thrilled with his increasing control (he'd been a premature ejaculator before). However, he never attributed his increasing sense of well-being to our unconventional lovemaking. He was sure it had to be because of some unknown factor. So he'd renege, ejaculate, and the trouble would start: over sensitivity, inconsiderate behavior, and misunderstandings. He tried to seduce a friend before my very eyes, lifting her off the ground, cuddling her, and asking for her phone number with me standing there. Even external events seemed to go wrong—our cars were towed or broken into, I lost my wallet *twice*, and so forth.

The final crash came in India where he joined me for a week while I was touring. He insisted I book the most expensive hotel in Delhi (against my advice) and he wanted to pay for it. Before he left our home city I'd asked him to promise that he wouldn't make the trip unless he would honor our agreement to avoid orgasm. He assured me—and then chose to ejaculate our first night together on the theory that, we should "do it my way sometimes, and your way sometimes."

At that point I snapped, and thought to myself. "Fine! You want great sex? You shall have it." I absolutely wore him out—I think we made love four times. And the following morning I demanded more. When we got out of bed he was a zombie. He wasn't up to touring the city. After a brief effort he retreated to the hotel cocktail lounge and spent the day there drinking and complaining about how expensive the hotel was. When I returned from sightseeing he asked me to pay half of the hotel costs. Our Indian guide confessed that he had never met a more unpleasant person than Costas.

Our trip was a disaster from that point. In fact, we went our separate ways shortly thereafter, until our flight home. And, to console myself, I ran up a credit card debt it took me two years to pay off. When we arrived at the airport he wouldn't even ride into the city in the same taxi though I had to stop at his apartment for my house keys.

Imagine my bewilderment when, only a few months later, I overheard him at a party explaining to others the benefits of ejaculation control....Life is funny, eh?

Here's the experience of another woman:

I got serious about learning to make love without orgasm long before I found your material. I read a tantra book that said women sometimes unconsciously engage in power plays by pushing their partners to ejaculate. And I have to say that I always got a thrill out of my partner's surrender in the throes of orgasm. I realize that men are subconsciously programmed to "spread it around," but I think we're programmed to be "sperm suckers."

One of my lovers had been in an ashram (celibate) for years. I couldn't help noticing his severe depression several days after we would make love. I'd begun to wonder if I was doing him a favor.

While I was struggling with this inner conflict I got a clear message that passion was a bad idea. A friend brought an attractive man to a party at my home. In our introductory conversation he told me all about his creative work—Lars was a gifted graphic designer. He was sensitive, sincere, courteous and somewhat shy. He was accompanied by a polite, but much older, woman, with whom I didn't speak much. I didn't realize they were lovers. A few weeks later the friend who had brought them both to my house showed up again. He was shattered; Lars was dead.

Apparently Lars had only been with the woman a few months. And during that time he'd had periods of utterly uncharacteristic, violent behavior. For example, he got into fights in bars and had even been threatened with arrest. My friend, who had known Lars' whole family for years, also talked to his lover after Lars' death. She told him Lars had also become sexually aggressive. The night of his death his lover had refused to participate. She went into another room to lie down. He came in later, sat on top of her, and demanded that she make love. She said, "no." He pulled a gun from behind his back and shot himself in the head.

Now, it's *possible* that there was no link whatsoever between his emotional/behavioral deterioration and his sex life. It was clear to me, though, that some sort of severe imbalance certainly

corresponded with the period of their intimacy. I promised myself to
stop using my sexiness to put others at risk.

A Woman's Guide to Male English [Further Studies]
- If he says, "Do you want to go to a movie?" it actually
  means "I'd eventually like to have sex with you."
- "Can I take you out to dinner?" *means* "I'd eventually like
  to have sex with you."
- "May I have this dance?" *means* "I'd eventually like to
  have sex with you."
- "What's wrong?" *means* "I guess sex tonight is out of
  the question."
- "You look tense. Let me give you a massage" *means* "I
  want to fondle you."

The Internet

Here's another "I learned the hard way" story:

**Your material really hit home for me. Over the past few years I've
been through two relationships with men who were close, trusted
friends for at least a year before we became lovers. I was in a
basement band with one of them and the other I'd shared a secretary
with before we became lovers. Both relationships "cratered" within
a month or two after sex entered the picture. I remember that, right
after we made love the first time, the second man said, "this was a
big mistake," but he couldn't explain why he felt uneasy.**

**I was sorry he felt that way but figured my love for him would
overcome it in due course—so I didn't push him. However, the next
time we made love he unnerved me again with, "I don't always have
to come, you know." This was a new one on me. I knew he loved
women—and sex—so I simply couldn't believe he meant it.**

**I did think maybe he was worried about impotence or something,
but I didn't want to rush into asking him about such a delicate
matter. Anyway, I doubted we'd have that problem. Selflessly**

giving pleasure was one of my great joys and, hey, I'd heard Dr. Ruth: "Orgasm = pleasure," so "lovemaking = orgasm," right? I thought to myself, "Of course you'll come! Don't worry, I'll take care of it." And I did. Quickly, though, it felt like he was seeing me in a different light. It's hard to say why I thought so. Once he bought me a very expensive gift and I received it as a gesture of love. This clearly made him uncomfortable.

Some days later it dawned on me that perhaps the gift had been tinged with a hint of payment, as if I were a mistress or something. I felt hurt. My favors are freely given not because I undervalue them but because they are beyond anyone's means to purchase. I made sure I asked for nothing—so it would be clear our relationship wasn't a business deal. I figured that if I just kept giving (massages, meals and so forth) things between us would shift back to the easy harmony we'd once had.

Instead it seemed like his uneasiness grew. Indeed, I had the impression that he would have preferred a clear "deal," because without one I registered as an enigma of whom he needed to be especially wary. Ouch! I loved this man without strings in the only ways I'd learned (i.e., emphasis on passion). Yet it felt like he no longer saw me accurately because of a mushrooming paranoia for which I lacked the antidote. It was painful and humiliating. And *Peace Between The Sheets* explains it all. What a relief to know there's a way around this separation problem. I no longer want to be "a great lover."

Often we discover we're ready to take a radically different tack when we hit (another) crisis. Here's the tale of Isaac and Susan:

Isaac: "I want a divorce." That was how I started the conversation. I wanted a spiritual life and was ready to move on until I could find purpose and eventually some light. Susan wanted to keep the relationship together, but I couldn't have cared less. I was over it.

After three days of discussion I finally gave in and proposed a possible solution. I had just read an earlier version of *Peace Between The Sheets*, and saw a stark picture of what I had been going through. I felt drained. I was irritable. I was all that the manuscript described.

We started into the *Exchanges*, me with a pretty resistant heart, and Susan with a surprising amount of love. First I ran into my fear of true love and acceptance—rather than just sexual love. Yet very quickly we dropped our boundaries and enjoyed a different intensity. Our lovemaking has given us both a release from the material natures we had fallen into. And our perspective and consciousness widen with our commitment to this method of relating sexually. I like the excitement without the energy loss.

We were soon the only couple in our couples' therapy group making progress. I even gave the therapist a copy of this material before we stopped attending. I am in deep gratitude for this work.

Susan: It seems as though all the relationships I have ever had began that downhill slide of separation shortly after the beginning. I was sick of the cycle and seriously considered celibacy as a solution. My marriage to Isaac, sadly, was no different. Fear of intimacy was driving us apart. Separation was the only solution that he saw for our deteriorating relationship. NO!...my mind screamed...not again!

That was when we came across this material. I saw how we were a classic example of nearly all of the symptoms mentioned. I figured we didn't have anything to lose. So we started the *Exchanges* with some skepticism. I was soon amazed at my feelings of tenderness for this man, who only a few days before was leaving me. My heart broke open! We were daring to walk down the path towards true intimacy, and how exciting it was/is.

Every night I looked forward to the *Exchanges* with much anticipation. We actually had fun and even learned to play....this was a new element in our relationship, and I loved every minute of it. We have been successfully practicing this way for months and our lives and our relationship are on the up, up, up!

The best part about it is that lovemaking WITHOUT orgasm is so much more of a turn-on than sex WITH orgasm! This has also given us a sense of connectedness with each other and with spirit that we didn't have before. Together, I feel, we are more grounded in our spiritual practices, which is the most important thing in my life.

Author's note: Within a year they bought a house together and he soon took a rewarding new job.

I asked a couple in their early 20's why they tried the *Exchanges*. Here's what Ian and Andrea said:

We had reached the point in our relationship when we wanted to experience each other sexually. When we did, it was luscious sex, but something was missing. Ian wasn't fully present with Andrea. He was paying more attention to insecurities and fantasies—which he soon realized were coming from a lot of exposure to pornography earlier in his life.

We figured out that the intention behind our lovemaking was wrong. We realized this when we felt emptiness after our encounters and experienced mood fluctuations in our feelings toward each other.

We took some time to *not* be sexual with each other—just cuddly and loving—so we could connect with our hearts. We reset our intentions to "LOVE" instead of "pleasure." The *Exchanges* allowed us to make *love* finally leaving us feeling infinitely pleasured and loved and whole.

Seek Not for the Solution in a World
from which the Answer Is Barred

Sexologists have been trained to explain that men who prefer to avoid ejaculation have problems. And they will say similar things about women who don't snap at every opportunity to come. They may be basing their advice on complaints they hear from clients who come to them because of problems with conventional sex. Apparently they hear a lot of complaints, too. 43% of women and 31% of men experience sexual difficulties.[47]

I think it will turn out that conventional sex is the culprit behind most of these difficulties, and that these troubles are clear signals that we're "doing it wrong." After all, at least 99% of sexual encounters take place without the intention to fertilize an ovum. When we insist on engaging in sexual behavior that drains us, it's like continuing to eat high calorie desserts because 1% of the population wants to gain weight.

If you've read this far, you've heard that men can recover from premature ejaculation or increase their libido, and women can grow more sexually responsive and avoid urinary tract infection with a different approach to sex. I believe statistical studies will one day bear these experiences out on a large scale.

Blind indulgence isn't the only definition of "normal" when it comes to sex. To be sure, someone who does not completely open physically and emotionally to his or her partner has blocked energy. Yet, as that block is often at the heart, frequent orgasm will, at best mask, rather than solve, any underlying uneasiness.

In my experience, a relationship based strictly on mutual caring and safety is a rapid, effective way to open your heart to your lover. As that happens, you both effortlessly attune to each other at very subtle levels. This makes your lovemaking as elegant as a ballet, but with the lighthearted flirtatiousness of a spring picnic *a deux* and the emotional depth of a great novel. I suspect this heightened sensitivity is the very key to satisfying ecstasy without energy hangovers.

To be sure, you will always have the option of using your newfound openness for conventional sex if you want to be *normal*, but that choice will also carry you back into a *natural* addictive cycle followed by the *usual* separation. So don't be afraid to chart new territory. The statistics will catch up with those of us who master this new approach.

> Statistics, as you know, is the most exact of false sciences.
>
> *Jean Cau*

Chapter 9
Bon Voyage

A man was walking along the beach in California. He came upon an ancient bottle that looked like it might have a genie in it. So he rubbed it, and, sure enough, a genie came out.

The genie said, "OK—one wish." The man thought for a long time. Eventually he said, "I love Hawaii, but I hate to fly. I'd like a bridge from the coast of California to Hawaii."

"Just my friggin' luck," whined the genie. "Dude...can't ya think of something else? I mean that's a lotta work. I'll have to drive pilings down to the sea floor for miles in some places. And it's a helluva long distance, too."

So the man thought some more. After a very long time, he said, "All right, I'd settle for the answer to three questions instead. "Why do women do the things they do, why do they think the way they do, and why *are* they the way they *are*?"

The genie got very quiet. Finally, he muttered, "2 lanes or 4 lanes?"   *The Internet*

If you're feeling adventurous, and ready to set sail on a healing journey, you may find the navigational aids in this chapter helpful. As has been explained biology pushes us into certain roles. It forces the man to exploit every possible fertilization opportunity and resist taking "no" for an answer. It leaves the woman in the equally forced role of law officer. She must do whatever it takes to keep the man in check if she doesn't want to have intercourse. This "keep sniffing till she stops growling" dynamic is perfect for dogs, but it won't work if you want to use sex to heal.

Of Boats and Pilots

Those who documented the existence of the relaxed, valley orgasm thousands of years ago opted for quite different roles. They advised that, during intercourse, the woman is the boat and the man is the pilot. The woman's role is to relax into total receptivity, which she obviously cannot do if she has to police her lover. The man's role is an effortless attentiveness, which he cannot deliver if he's blind with impulsive behavior. Instead of rowing he merely steers. And it is his function to know exactly where his boat is at all times—that is, the degree to which his partner is aroused—so they can journey safely.

In addition to this new flow of energy where the woman opens as the man guides, there are certain other factors that make for safe boating. The key to a man's becoming an infallible pilot rests with the woman. If she is open and loving, he will find it easy to maintain complete control. Likewise, the man holds the key to her receptivity. If she knows she's in the hands of a safe pilot she can melt easily.

The solution to this apparent "chicken or egg" puzzle is time. After years of conventional sex few of us can instantly open our hearts or pilot with absolute safety. So the *Exchanges* call for a two-week period where there is lots of snuggling and no intercourse. Time is your friend. You will see progress rapidly, yet it takes time to thoroughly master a new practice. So relax and enjoy the re-patterning process.

Q:	Why are men's brains larger than dogs'?
A:	So they don't hump women's legs at cocktail parties.

What to Expect

People are often surprised by the fact that making love this way demands no technical mastery. Instead it requires patience, sustained intimacy, and a willingness to stop pursuing physical gratification. In my experience, authentic love soon flowers between partners in the presence of these ingredients. This is why I advise singles who want to try this to find a partner who is enthusiastic about these ideas, rather than someone with whom they are infatuated. Infatuation muddies motives and usually causes someone to bend the rules.

> **Temptation is the dress rehearsal for a karmic experience of negativity.** *Gary Zukov*

For the first few nights of the *Exchanges* lovers often require special consideration. Those who have been without partners for a while—especially men—can have intense reactions to intimate contact. As one man to whom I described the *Exchanges* said, "I won't be able to sleep next to a woman—I'll be awake all night." And the fact is, he might. Yet if you both stick with the recipe this restlessness will pass within a few days.

Some men swing the opposite way. Before they can reach a balanced state of well-being their main spring has to unwind. One of my friend's lovers, a very dynamic businessman who had been on his own for a long time, spent most of their first few days simply sleeping—to his chagrin. The benefits of this approach, however, come from achieving an inner balance, so adjustments like temporary restlessness or fatigue are perfectly normal. After an initial adjustment, well-being prevails. Even people who slept poorly on their own, frequently find they sleep far better with a partner.

So whoever is feeling most centered should willingly put his or her needs aside for a few days. Though it may not feel like it when you're sleep-deprived, your greatest need is for a centered partner. Give him or her "all you can eat" of selfless, non-erotic attention. Your generosity will return to you in the form of a balanced, energetic, attentive partner.

> There are a number of mechanical devices which increase sexual arousal, particularly in women. Chief among these is the Mercedes-Benz 380SL convertible. *P. J. O'Rourke*

Not So Harmless Activities

Once again, this is a different approach to sexual intimacy. The goal is not just intercourse or a dopamine rush of sexual excitement. The goal is the healing that comes from two open hearts. As you may recall from Chapter 3, an open heart promotes the ideal balance of body chemicals, which automatically ensures sexual arousal. In other words, when you have taken a slow approach and your hearts are truly fear-free your genitals will be ready. Ready genitals, alone, do not necessarily indicate open hearts, as our primitive brains can induce performance even while subconscious fear reigns.

One friend said I ought to call this book, *"No Viagra®, No K-Y Jelly®"* because sexual arousal becomes so effortless. Yet the reason it is effortless is that you never force it. Ever. Even if your partner was very aroused last time. Even if your partner would respond rapidly to deliberate stimulation. Just wait...until another occasion. If you follow this simple rule you will find you hardly ever have to wait. So conventional foreplay, Viagra®, vibrators, and anything else that artificially stimulates sexual performance are unwise. Even tongue kissing should wait until after the first few days of the *Exchanges.*

Of course, either partner should feel free to initiate selfless, nurturing touch (as opposed to hungry touch). But, again, if you are a man, never have intercourse unless your partner's genitals are lubricating naturally without physical stimulation—even if she kidnaps your penis. Just rescue it and reassure her with loving affection. She cannot benefit you by having intercourse too soon because, unless her magnet of sexual desire is fully operational, a nourishing current will not flow between you. Forced intercourse, in fact, encourages a heart/genital split.

By the same token, if you are a woman, never initiate intercourse— unless your partner has signaled his total enthusiasm and is waiting for you to do the honors. If you indicate you want intercourse "now," he will do his best to oblige you, even if he is not truly ready. He is likely to force his performance with fantasy or vigorous stimulation. Yet his penis will do you no good if his heart isn't fully open yet. So wait.

Get a Lollipop

"I'm a very oral person...and I'm not talkin' about talkin'," said a friend.

Sorry, Tiger. Years of experience and frustration have revealed the unwelcome, but simple, truth: however clear your intentions when you crawl into each other's arms, if you engage in certain activities, your biological auto-pilots will take over. Most people view activities such as dressing in lacy underwear, crawling all over a partner naked, posing nude, frenzied kissing, rubbing genitals on a partner, oral sex, viewing porn, and so forth as harmless. And it seems like they must fit into the picture of healing sexuality somehow.

In fact, however, they don't fit into the picture of healing sexuality. Innocent and enjoyable as they may be, they actually prevent you from finding the heart-centered ecstasy you are now seeking by pulling all your attention swiftly toward the physical gratification of the urge they awaken in your primitive brain. The good news is that with this other approach intercourse and kissing become increasingly pleasurable. So once you recover from your dopamine rush addiction you won't miss your former habits. Promise.

Before leaving the subject of the not-so-harmless, I want to share the remarks of another friend. She told me she didn't want to learn this way of making love because she enjoys being such an accomplished lover—and she'd never get to show off her skills. Yet when she left her last boyfriend it was "because I didn't want to be f**ked like a porn star." If you want to use sex to heal, dismiss your inner temptress. She attracts equally performance-oriented partners.

It's OK, George

"Sex at age 90 is like trying to shoot pool with a rope."

George Burns

The experience you are now seeking is not dependent upon

127

sustaining an erection. Erections come and go, but the exhilarating exchange of affection on which the benefits of this approach depend is unaffected. This is because a powerful "electricity" is actually flowing between two open hearts.

Intercourse is a reflection of a deep desire to merge, but genitals do not cause desire. Rather, desire develops naturally once all uneasiness is gone. Barry Long, Australian advocate of sacred sex, says that a period of sexual unresponsiveness is natural as we move back into our hearts. It passes when we heal the heart/genital split of the past. So let your genitals show you when this split has healed.

Forced performance would merely over-ride any uneasiness about intimacy itself. So it's better to stick to non-performance oriented, loving contact for weeks, if necessary, to allow your sexual energy to arise spontaneously. Then heart and genitals operate in tandem.

To Have All, Give All

Up until now your improved health, career progress and spiritual goals have seemed to hinge on time spent pursuing them—at the expense of other activities. When you create a healing sexual relationship, however, you leave behind the sense of scarcity on which such struggles rest. You plug into a far more effective means of creating balance, well-being, abundance and heightened spiritual awareness. It's based on giving.

When you give, you program your subconscious for abundance. You convince it that you have enough to give and it begins to react accordingly. Experience it for yourself. While you do the *Exchanges*, make it a point to be extremely generous. Remember, actions count; so don't just measure your devotion in "I love you's," tears of joy, or hours logged in the sack.

Shifting your partner to top priority doesn't mean you'll have no time for your other activities. In fact, you'll swiftly enter a flow that will allow you both to accomplish more than ever without having to negotiate at all. But it happens because of inner harmony and inner harmony is a product of generously caring for another. So start by voluntarily putting your partner's well-being before your other goals even if you have to break some cherished routines. A rock solid relationship is built on knowing you can count on each other...no matter what. If you don't know if you can count on your partner then no other evidence of his or her love amounts to much. If you do know it, you'll find you *want* to accommodate each other's other interests whenever possible.

No Other Agendas
You can only open your heart fully to someone if you perceive they have *your* best interests at heart.

Unfortunately, you may have spent years in draining relationships that caused you to anxiously guard your time and income from your intimate partner. So even if you now understand why you want to give, your giving skills may be a bit rusty. Here are some suggestions to help kick start you while you try the *Exchanges*.

- Take turns treating each other to things. Splitting is not giving.
- Make gifts to each other. Material gifts are appropriate but non-material gifts can be even more expressive.
- Treat each other like royalty. For example, never enter a room without checking in with your partner with a smile, a word, or a touch, if possible.
- Be creative spoiling each other with unexpected acts of thoughtfulness:
  - Clean the pan your partner burned the dinner in
  - Suggest an outing or music you know your partner would enjoy
  - Give a spontaneous massage
  - Fill the car with gas even if it's your partner's car, and not your job
  - Put toothpaste on your partner's toothbrush at bedtime
  - Write a mushy poem or note
  - Prepare a favorite dish

- Leave your partner a surprise treat

When your only goal is to pamper another it makes you feel whole and strong. Nothing is missing. It is the most reliable way to fill the empty hole inside that you may have been trying to fill by focusing on your own goals.

Avoid touching your partner when you are coming from a place of hunger. It can make your partner feel like he is being devoured, or like she's stuck nursing a greedy baby. This is a stressful experience. Shift gears and focus on your partner's well-being instead. Nurture your partner and he or she will nourish you beyond your expectations.

What About Birth Control? **By all means, use it.** In theory it only takes one sperm to bring another being back into matter. In fact, however, it takes a fair number of sperm to penetrate the membrane of an ovum. Some have not used birth control since they began making love without ejaculation years ago, and have not had an unwanted pregnancy. Making love without artificial anything (or worrying about fertility cycles) feels like a visit to the Garden of Eden. Yet, pregnancy without noticeable ejaculation is possible, so take any necessary precautions. Making love without ejaculation is a true blessing for men. It increases their joint control over the procreation process. With this approach a couple rarely gets pregnant unless both parties agree. Best of all, when we all master healing sex we won't have to listen to the ear-splitting squawks of the "pro-choicers" and "right-to-lifers." Without unwanted pregnancies there's nothing to fight about.

"What If I Have Very Little Sexual Control?"

The *Exchanges* seem to be extremely effective in helping people, especially men, gain complete control. For at least two weeks intercourse is not even an option, so you can relax completely and turn your attention to your partner's comfort and healing. You will also feel your partner's attentions more powerfully while relaxed. This exchange of caring attention balances you both, and balance spells effortless control.

When you enter the intercourse phase of the *Exchanges*, the emphasis will be on motionless, affectionate contact, which also makes control less challenging. Meanwhile, here are some other activities that can strengthen your inner balance:

- Deep forgiveness of all past hurts inflicted by the opposite sex.
- Avoiding masturbation and sexual fantasy, and turning one's attention to helping others instead. (Let your energy flow up through your heart instead of out through your genitals.)
- Preceding intimacy with rigorous exercise, meditation, a warm bath, or a practice such as yoga or tai chi.

Advice for Wilted Plants

Strange to say, one of the traits that can motivate you to reach for higher quality relationships, that is, your love of excellence, can also be a huge stumbling block. Many of us want to be perfect for each other before we take the medicine of the *Exchanges*. We want to deny our insecurities, hide our addictions, and live up to some imagined description of each other's perfect mate. This outlook is understandable, but misguided. The only high standard you need to maintain is integrity. That is, stick to the *Exchanges*.

As for your other noble aspirations, it's better if you set out together strictly as you are—with all your current "warts" exposed. This frees your partner to do the same. Warts, after all, are there to be healed, and healing is the sole focus of this approach to sex. So if you have an addiction, a sharp tongue, or a fear of abandonment, admit it. You, like everyone else on this planet, are a wilted plant for the moment. That's okay. Self-doubts, too, are normal. Making love differently will change things for the better, but don't pretend to be something you aren't in advance of genuine progress. Each improvement will give you something to celebrate together.

If you have a serious addiction—to anything—be optimistic. Many heart-centered people on this planet suffer from addictions. It is a perfectly understandable response to the pain of separation that currently infects us. But addiction is like a mistress. It's a device that sabotages the deep intimacy you are now seeking. So you will not be able to keep your addiction if you want a healing relationship.

If you are clear that you wish to let go of your addiction, the *Exchanges* offer superb support. If you cooperate fully by (1) avoiding passion and the brain chemistry that accompanies it, and (2) refusing to separate from your lover overnight to pursue your addiction in private, the *Exchanges* will directly heal the isolation (lack of wholeness) that is driving your addiction. With a steady supply of loving nourishment you will soon be strong enough to release the unhealthy self pity that also feeds it.

When you begin the *Exchanges,* stop your addiction "cold turkey," and follow them exactly. Beware that for a while, a foreign will (born of a past drive to meet your addiction no matter how destructive your actions), will attempt to control you. It will do its best to convince you that you want to "cheat" on the *Exchanges* and return to passion in your love making, that you are too weak to succeed, or that you should separate from your lover to do your own thing. All are just invalid excuses for resuming your addiction. They do not reflect your true will. Prayer or meditation can strengthen your inner resolve.

And if you fall back into your addiction, do not use it as an excuse to have an orgasm or separate from your lover, too. When you are clear simply drop your addiction and pick up the *Exchanges* again. Don't try to do an *Exchange* while under the influence of your addiction, but spend each night together, even if you relapse.

If your partner is fighting an addiction accept that he/she must heal it. Your role is merely to hold an unconditionally loving space in which the healing can take place. As long as your partner sticks to the *Exchanges*, be encouraging, forgiving, generous, non-judgmental and affectionate—but stay detached from the outcome. It is not within your control.

NOTE: if you cannot do an *Exchange*, except when under the influence of alcohol, marijuana and other foreign substances, you are not ready. Wait until your addiction is no longer your top priority—and union is. Find a 12 Step Program. There's one available for nearly every symptom of life here on Planet Separation.

A True Life Story

Once you grasp the principles it's tempting to design your own version of healing sex. Unfortunately, if you trust your instincts, you will unwittingly tend to retain your defenses against true intimacy. A 23 year old colleague, who does a lot of meditation and yoga, was really inspired by these ideas. One day he appeared at my door, glowing. "I've just made love for four and a half hours to my friend who's visiting from Alaska for a week. It was perfect and definitely a spiritual experience. Thank you so much for letting me read your material, Liz! It did "lose it" at the end, but that was perfect, too."

"Great, Rich." After he left, I asked myself what he had read. There was certainly no commitment to a month-long approach, he had taken no time to build up an energy balance between them, and, of course, he had ejaculated. I resolved to record what unfolded. During the rest of her brief visit his sexual control dropped off radically, and the more orgasms that occurred, the more the glow faded. Shortly after she left he stepped on a nail and hurt his foot. Then his car had a flat that had to be repaired in a place that was an hour from the nearest town. (Those readers who've studied metaphysics will be familiar with the concept that our inner state controls our external experience—somewhat as a film determines what we see on a movie screen. So an inner sense of depletion manifests as draining events.)

133

The following week he was noticeably irritable at work, and when I asked about it, he confessed, "she's in love with me, and she might be coming back to work here. Now we'll see what kind of hole I dug for myself." I couldn't help noticing that he was thinking in terms of "loss" and "feeling cornered" rather than "union" and "spiritual encounter."

He cheered up significantly when she announced that she could only come back for one week the following month. Before her arrival, however, he got involved with a second woman—without mentioning to her that "Number 1" was returning. He started to question his own integrity, as he wasn't meeting his high standards. And when "Number 2" learned of her competition she was only too happy to help point out his flaws. Meanwhile he incurred about $1100 of additional, unexpected car repairs that put him in debt—something he'd carefully been avoiding.

And just about the time he resolved to get serious about managing his sexual energy strictly for a higher end, "Number 1" returned in lust overdrive because of the great sex they'd had before. She took personally his decision to go more slowly and was furious. When, at last, she departed—after various attempts at emotional blackmail—he said, "I really love her, but I feel relieved."

This scenario will sound familiar to anyone who has been struggling to combine loving connections with passion quests. I chose it because it shows how easy it is to become an "Intensity Junkie" while the primitive brain rules us. Even with the best intentions you can't lay down a new subconscious response to sexual intimacy overnight. It's not enough to grasp the beauty of the idea and run with it. You need time and structure to recondition your responses to sexual intimacy. So if you are ready to try a fresh approach, use the *Exchanges* in the second half of this book. They will improve your chances of success.

Fleas In A Jar

I once read that if you put fleas in a jar and put the lid on they will try to jump out. After they hit the lid a few times, though, they adjust the

134

height of their jumps to a level just short of the lid. Then, if you remove the lid, they will continue to restrict the height of their jumps to just short of where the lid was. In other words, they won't escape, even though they're free to go.

Biology has successfully convinced us that we're fleas in a jar. Conventional sex causes us to bang ourselves repeatedly on the painful lid of estrangement between lovers. It's no wonder we make choices as stiffling as those hopeless fleas did. Maybe we withdraw from relationships altogether, or choose indulgence at enormous emotional and material cost, or settle for deadening, but less draining, relationships. All are blind alleys, so, like our ancestors, most of us conclude there's no way to express our life force energy enthusiastically without wreaking havoc. As we shutdown, the world begins to look like a very depressing place. Worse yet, an unlimited amount of desperately needed enthusiasm, creativity and caring are lost to us all.

The truth is that there *is* no lid on the jar. By allowing biology to lead us around by the genitals we have unwittingly conspired with it to create the illusion of a prison.

Discover the truth. Take the hand of a willing partner and jump as high as you can. True freedom awaits. And thank you for your willingness to heal. Your efforts to find peace between the sheets can make a vital contribution to eradicating the heart-rending virus of separation.

PART II
THE ECSTATIC EXCHANGES

All the joy the world contains
has come through wishing happiness for others.
All the misery the world contains
has come through wanting pleasure for oneself.

Shantideva
9th Century Sage

What Are the Ecstatic Exchanges?

When all else fails...try the instructions.

The *Exchanges* are a recipe for changing the way we make love so we can use our relationships to heal. They consist of activities couples do together, arranged in a set format. Their goal is to create a cocoon of comfort and safety for you both—without any fear-producing associations. This allows you to re-pattern your subconscious.

The *Exchanges* were inspired by much trial and many errors and are offered in the hope that you will not have to repeat the blunders others have already made for you. So try them with an open mind. You can always return to your old habits afterward if not fully satisfied.

Structure

The *Exchanges* are divided into two *Phases*. The first, the *Nurturing Phase,* is primarily a "clothing on" *Phase.* Some of the *Exchanges* in the second, the *Stillness Phase,* include intercourse. So if you need to discuss birth control issues, or arrange for medical tests, do so now. Stay in a *Phase* until you have completed all of its *Exchanges.*

Each *Exchange* begins with some information and various preliminaries. Some couples prefer to customize their preliminary routine with spiritual readings or practices. The preliminaries are followed by an *"Activity"* and *"Snuggle."* Everyone prefers some the *Activities* to others, but be playful and try them all. (If you have a sound reason for omitting a particular *Activity*—such as a physical handicap—substitute another *Activity* from the list of *Additional Activities* at the end of the book.)

The *Exchanges* intentionally call for a gradual increase in physical intimacy. If you exceed their pace you defeat their power to replace subconscious uneasiness with contentment. Make an effort to do one *Exchange* a day, but trust the flow of events. However, do your best to complete the first 14 (the *Nurturing Phase*) in less than four weeks.

137

Intercourse is very nourishing so you don't want to delay it indefinitely. It is also ideal if you can go away together for the seven days of the second *Phase*.

Think *Healing*, Not *Sex*

It helps to adopt a mindset of "this is not about sex; it's about healing each other." Remember, the goal is to re-pattern your subconscious. You are shifting the conventional associations between sex and addiction to associations between sex and mutual feelings of giving, gratitude, ease and peace. As explained in Chapter 4, the first one is the equivalent of a drug high that leads to a hangover that separates, while the second is a *heart* high that increases your sense of well-being and desire for union.

The *Exchanges* themselves are simple, relaxed and not especially demanding. They call for no bizarre positions or other performance challenges. They are designed to allow you to feel secure and relaxed with each other as you open to deeper intimacy. If you choose to cheat by thrusting or crawling on top of your partner when it is not advised it's because your primitive brain is angling for an "accidental" crash, which will imperil the intimacy building between you. Conventional foreplay and sex are also compelling because they rapidly create the emotional distance that your "Intimacy Sabotaging Device" finds comforting.

You are now attempting to heal the fear of intimacy behind the urge for separation. It only succumbs to regular loving contact without passion. Be consistent so you can evaluate the *Exchanges'* benefits objectively. Respond to the restless Voice of Temptation by dropping back to the first *Exchange*, or simply holding each other in spoon position—rather than dropping back into old habits.

Suggestions

There's no need to read all of the *Exchanges* before beginning, but as you go forward, read each new *Exchange* out loud as they often call for discussion. They may be done at any time during the day or night.

Natural lighting, such as a candle or open fire, enriches evening experiences. The lengths sometimes suggested for activities are minimums. If you wish to time your activities try using music of a suitable length rather than watches or clocks.

The *Exchanges* call for a spirit of playfulness that flowers in complete privacy, without interruption. Ensure that children, pagers, pets, phones and visitors will not lead to distractions. Take turns preparing the environment with gentle music, pleasant scents, extra pillows, massage oil and non-alcoholic, natural beverages.

On days you aren't ready to begin a new *Exchange* make sure you still do a *Snuggle* before falling asleep. Otherwise you are separating physically. That's when emotional separation often blossoms and communication declines.

What if you feel like snuggling when you aren't officially "doing an *Exchange*?" Enjoy! But stay within the limits of intimacy of the *Exchanges* you've completed safely. For example, avoid disrobing or genital contact ahead of schedule. Also resist vigorously rubbing your genitals on your partner or reaching into your partner's clothing. "Feeding frenzy" behavior will leave you hungrier than ever. If you focus, instead, on your gratitude for having your partner in your arms, and pamper one another, you'll find your encounters surprisingly fulfilling.

It is also helpful to avoid rich, heavy meals, caffeine, alcohol and other substances that alter natural feelings at least for two hours immediately before your encounters, if not entirely. Substances that alter clarity can sabotage the best of intentions. A diet that relies heavily on fresh fruit and vegetables and contains little meat and dairy may also help you experience heightened states more easily. In general, try to allow an hour or two after eating before each *Exchange*.

Some *Exchanges* take time. If you don't feel calm, clear, and ready, simply repeat an earlier "*Snuggle.*" Only do a new *Exchange* when you are both feeling adventurous.

If possible, ask another couple you think might enjoy the *Exchanges* to begin them when you do. It can be very helpful to share regular feedback with others who are trying to reorient their lovemaking. Make no effort to stay on the same schedule as your friends, however.

Intimacy builds rapidly using the *Exchanges*, but there's no need to spend every minute together. Instead why not use the energy you are creating to do something you've been putting off? Express your creativity, cheer a sick friend, do a brilliant job at work, study with intense concentration or clean out a closet. Your increasing inspiration and efficiency may surprise you.

Make your partner the prime focus of your nurturing. You're helping each other open your hearts. It's nearly impossible to rediscover a healthy vulnerability if one of you is chatting on the phone regularly to a former lover. The future may move you apart, but let the present be a focus on genuine togetherness.

Do not masturbate before beginning the Exchanges. It's logical, but mistaken, to assume that if you decrease the pressure you'll be more at ease during the *Exchanges*. Instead, try a new approach to gaining peace of mind: mutual nurturing. (See Chapter 2.)

Special Circumstances

• *What if you have only a few days to spend together?*

Despite the benefits of intimacy, it can be surprisingly painful to start the *Exchanges* in a futureless situation, or "non-relationship." They work quickly, creating a powerful desire for more closeness. When it is not forthcoming it's distressing. So it is not advisable to use them in such circumstances.

If you choose to start them anyway don't skip any. Resign yourselves to the shallow end of the pool. Deep diving ahead of schedule opens you up too quickly. It will leave you acutely uncomfortable in the weeks following your imminent separation in ways you cannot foresee or prevent. You may, for example, experience dream orgasms or a severe sense of deprivation. So stick to the *Exchanges* in order. And if you find yourselves together in the future begin again at the beginning. Let stable harmony, rather than traditional consummation, be your goal. You'll both be stronger, happier and more deeply satisfied.

- *What if you're in an established relationship?*

You face a challenge. For the period of time you experiment with the *Exchanges* accept that the purpose of your relationship is radically different. Whereas hunger and discharge of energy, or comfortable stagnation, may have played major roles before, determined giving and careful protection of each other's well-being now command center stage. This can be disorienting.

To make the adjustment easily take a moment to get back in touch with the tingly feelings you had for each other when you first met and began flirting—before you ever had sex. You might each separately write down at least three adjectives that describe how you were feeling at that time and then tell each other. Take the *Exchanges* step-by-step. Even if you think you are as familiar to each other as old slippers, surprises are in store.

- *What if you have an addiction?*

See Chapter 9, "Bon Voyage," the section entitled, "Advice for Wilted Plants." For this purpose, frequent use of marijuana is an "addiction" because it tends to weaken willpower and promote irresponsible rationalizations for yielding to cravings.

The Nurturing Phase
Opening the Heart
(14 Exchanges)

Are you ready? To find out, use the checklist below. Experience has shown that the first two items require special awareness.

Readiness Checklist

His Hers

☐ ☐ **I am prepared to spend the entire night, every night, with my partner while doing the *Exchanges*.** If you can't commit to this, the physical separation in your relationship will leave your old patterns unhealed. It would be best to defer sex, or stick to conventional sex, until you can make this commitment.

_____ (HIS) **My last genital orgasm (whether during dream,**
(date) **masturbation, or intercourse) occurred on this date**
☐ ←**or was more than two weeks ago.**

_____ (HERS) **My last genital orgasm (whether during dream,**
(date) **masturbation, or intercourse) occurred on this date**
☐ ←**or was more than two weeks ago.**

It is ideal if you can wait to begin the *Exchanges* until it has been at least two weeks since either of you had a genital orgasm. Orgasm temporarily clouds perception and weakens desire for lasting intimacy. It also strengthens a craving for hot sex, hampering your ability to heal each other selflessly.

Some of us cannot get past our orgasm addiction, however, without a partner's loving energy. So if you wish to begin immediately you may. Just stay within the boundaries of the *Exchanges*. Expect biology to dictate unsound instructions to you for about two weeks. Ignore them. Do not lie on top of your partner until the two weeks have passed.

☐ ☐ I am not intimately involved with anyone other than my partner. I am willing to be monogamous while trying the *Exchanges.*

☐ ☐ If I am addicted to drugs, alcohol, or anything else I could use to keep from committing myself completely to my primary relationship, I will give it up while trying the *Exchanges.* If I backslide on the addiction I will still spend every night with my partner, but I will not try to do an *Exchange* while my clarity is impaired.

☐ ☐ While we are doing the *Exchanges* together, I will give selflessly to my lover on every level, in and out of the bedroom. I understand that if I don't do this I will unconsciously drain my partner, defeating the purpose of the *Exchanges.*

☐ ☐ My motive is to heal. I am not using the *Exchanges* as an excuse to seduce my partner. Yet I also understand we may not be each other's ultimate partners, so I will let go of our physical relationship and move on without rancor if appropriate.

☐ ☐ I understand I can end my participation at any time, but I agree to inform my partner outside the bedroom, before I begin the next *Exchange,* if I decide I don't want to continue.

☐ ☐ Even if I don't feel like doing a new *Exchange,* I will do a non-intercourse *Snuggle* before falling asleep.

☐ ☐ I recognize that the goal of the *Exchanges* is to heal, rather than preserve, all forms of subconscious uneasiness between the sexes induced by mankind's primitive brain. Therefore, I realize that the *Exchanges* are not recommended for same sex partners—any balance achieved is likely to be too fragile for long-term results.

☐ ☐ I will remain at a level of intimacy I am comfortable with and only go forward when I feel ready. I will not push my partner to go faster.

□ □ **I am willing for my relationship to be a source of comfort and healing, and I will let go of all expectations/past learning to try this new approach.**

If you can check "yes" to all of these, you are ready. If not, your experience of the *Exchanges* is likely to be mixed. It would be better if you didn't try them.

Suggestions for Phase One

Cover up. As you are just beginning the *Exchanges* there may be a temptation to combine visual stimulation with the joy of closeness. This can be true because you've been too long deprived of intimate contact or it may happen because you're in a rut, born of past sexual habits that made visual stimulation a "rewarding" biological trigger.

The cure is simple: keep some clothing on for the *Nurturing Phase* of the *Exchanges* even if you have already seen each other nude. An exchange of loving energy occurs even through fabric. Let it surprise you. It, not your vision, is the key to feeling deeply nourished. Visual stimulation tends to leave you hungry. Gentle touch lets you give (allowing you to feel whole).

Men are often warmer than women. If he is in the habit of sleeping in the nude he may remove his underwear when he's ready to fall asleep— and replace it upon waking. She should keep a tee shirt and underwear on, however, throughout this *Phase*.

Keep cool. Hugging and even rolling around on each other affectionately seems to cause little problem while some clothing is on. Forceful thrusting, or simulating conventional intercourse, though, is ill advised even with clothing on. It can ignite an insatiable, grabby mentality and trigger defensive feelings. It's impossible to stay in your heart when all you can think about is how much you want to climax. So don't intentionally heat each other up. (And do not roll around on each other until two weeks have passed after either partner's last peak orgasm.)

If you are feeling especially energetic release the pressure by dancing together, wrestling playfully (unless it makes you feel unsafe), or exercising or stretching together.

Circulate energy. If you feel uncomfortably aroused after or during an *Exchange*, circulate your sexual energy to regain your peace of mind. Simply close your eyes, tighten the muscles around your perineum, and "draw" the energy up your spine to the top of your head as you inhale. Then imagine storing it in your navel. A few of these deep breaths will restore your composure.

Be a guardian. Experience has shown that it's best if one partner acts as a Watch Dog for each *Exchange*—otherwise, no one wants to say, "whoa." If the Watch Dog senses the temperature rising too rapidly he or she takes whatever measures are necessary to cool things down. Suggested techniques are:

- Vigorously scratching or rubbing your partner's scalp. This feels good and moves everyone's attention upward.
- Holding your partner in spoon and resting a hand lovingly on his penis, or her chest, until things calm down.
- Quietly saying, "inhale" and then sitting up straight, or lying together in each other's arms, breathing deeply and slowly and circulating your energy until you are calm and centered.
- Sitting next to your reclining partner and lightly, gently stroking his or her torso, arms and legs, avoiding genitals
- Cracking a joke to halt the momentum
- Gently stroking his or her face with love
- Looking into each other's eyes
- Meditating or praying for inner peace
- Touching the space over each other's heart

- Having your partner lie, face up, in front of you as you sit at his/her head, and resting your partner's head in your cradled hands without moving

Historical note: extreme measures can be appropriate. The Taoist lovemaking manuals suggested keeping a bowl of ice water by the bed for him to dip his penis in....So do whatever it takes!

Relax. Remember, your primitive brain has an agenda when you're in bed with a lover. If you want to regain control of your love life stop striving. Let your intimacy be as unforced as breathing.

Be patient. It is not unusual for the first *Phase* to go on for more than two weeks, so enjoy this time together as you wait for your sexual energy to stabilize. Remember that you may substitute new *Activities* from the end of book while you wait. If you have to back up don't stop doing *Activities*. They will keep in place the correct flow of energy between you, that is, lighthearted mutual giving.

Foul Weather Warning

If either of you has a genital orgasm during this *Phase*, you should remain in this *Phase* for two weeks beyond the orgasm, with some clothing on, still doing an *Activity* or *Snuggle* each day. Dream orgasms count, too. Often they signal that energy is flowing backward. That is, one (or both) of you is still draining the other at an energy level. Usually the "taking" shows up as a goal-oriented search for more physical gratification—even if you both manage to avoid an orgasm while awake.

During the two weeks or so following the orgasm you can expect inexplicable mood swings, mysterious fatigue, and distancing behavior on both your parts. Tears, over-reactions, icy silence, hurt feelings, feeling victimized, loss of courage, resurgence of old addictions, cynicism, draining physical discomforts and flaring tempers are likely. So is a desire to "stop all this nonsense and return to good old fashioned conventional sex." These unwelcome behaviors may be barely noticeable at first, but they worsen for about two weeks—and can even surprise you with a few nasty aftershocks beyond that time.

Remember: you and your partner are just suffering from a biological hangover. Its purpose is to discourage you, separate you, and convince you there's nothing you can do to outwit biology—until your next incarnation. Reach for your full potential now instead of giving up. The hangover will pass within a few weeks if you stay close, remain generous toward one another, and move beyond your old habits.

There's no doubt that an inadvertent genital orgasm is a major setback. For weeks afterward you tend to be out of synch with each other. If you feel an overwhelming need to give your partner an ultimatum relating to unacceptable behavior, or simply bolt, trust that you are oversensitive and overreacting. Get quiet and be patient. Stick around. (See Chapter 5 for additional tips.)

Exchange 1
WHICH WAY DOES YOUR CURRENT FLOW?

But there's a huge difference between your hugs and his. When you hug me I feel like you're hugging me for *me*. You want to comfort me and make me feel loved and lovable. When *he* hugs me I feel like he's hugging me for *him*. He wants to get his hands all over me because it turns *him* on.

As soon as you grasp that there are two types of touching—giving and grabbing—you have the key to healing each other. Two physical touches may look the same and yet have totally different effects depending upon the energy flow behind the touch. Only touches with your partner's best interests at heart will lead to true satisfaction. Intention is far more important than what you touch or how intimate the touch is.

If you affectionately nibble your partner's ear, or stroke your partner lovingly, his or her heart will open rapidly. If you seductively lick your partner's ear, or stroke your partner's genitals with the intention of heating your partner or yourself up sexually, you will destabilize your partner's energy and put yourselves back in the addiction cycle. Stay mindful of your intentions and consciously upgrade them—instead of trying to get away with a little something more than the *Exchanges* call for. Cheating has a tendency to lead to more cheating and it ultimately creates resentment...or regret.

The *Exchanges* take a very slow approach to physical intimacy because most of us have not learned to distinguish clearly between generous touch and greedy touch. We are wired to fan the flames of passion— which makes us increasingly unconscious and, therefore, selfish. We need time and water wings until we can stay afloat in the tempting undertow of sexual arousal. Clearly defined limits keep us safe while we learn to feel which way our energy is flowing in each moment and allow our conditioned responses to re-pattern.

One couple found that it was easier to set a clear intention if they began by touching each other over the heart before any other touching. Loving hugs are also a good place to start. So is looking into each other's eyes or a brief meditation while touching. Make sure your partner is there with you, consciously feeling your love and returning it, before expanding the range of your touch.

Otherwise you may find yourself fondling flesh with "no one home." That can lead to a disconcerting sense of loneliness, resentment, closed hearts, sexual fantasy and so forth. It can destabilize the energy between you and you will slow your progress if someone has an orgasm as a result. In short, every touch counts.

Suggested Preparation

Sounds: Beautiful, peaceful music in the background.

Time Out: He should lie, face up, with his head near her. She should cradle his head in her hands, with her palms resting on the surface beneath his head, and be still for about 5 minutes. He should just take deep breaths as she sends him loving energy through her hands.

Watch Dog: For this *Exchange,* **she** is the Dog.

Attire: Comfortable shirts and comfortable shorts or modest underwear. Bikinis or boxers that promote peeping, or over-stimulated genitals defeat the purpose of covering up. If too warm, he may remove his shirt.

ACTIVITY

- Just juicy hugs. Try hugging standing up, kneeling, and then in various seated positions, and finally horizontal hugs (not on top of each other, though).

- See if you can notice when your intention is to comfort and adore your partner from the heart and when it is tinged with thrill seeking.

- See if you can notice this subtle change in your partner's hugs, too.

- Remember, this time, just hugs—no other touching and no open-mouth kissing.

THE SNUGGLE

- Relax in each other's arms. Try spoon position. The person who most wants to be held should take the inside position. Whoever is on the outside, can place his/her hand on the other's chest *over the clothes*. If he is feeling over-stimulated, she can hold him and rest her hand lovingly on his penis *over his clothes,* without stimulating him, as she holds him in spoon position. This is surprisingly calming and satisfying, and can help him get comfortable with loving contact even when his penis also relaxes. Fall asleep if you wish.

- At night, if you awaken, ask your partner, with a touch, to hold you. And if asked, hold your partner—despite your sleepiness. Do not feel obliged to respond with activity but assure your partner that there is an endless supply of loving attention available. For, indeed, hugs are an inexhaustible natural resource.

Exchange 2
SILENT SATISFACTION

The *Exchanges* will gradually bring your level of sexual desire into harmony with your lover's. At first, though, you may find that one of you sometimes has considerably more desire than the other. Demanding urges are the product of insufficient loving contact, while defensive, chilly responses result from being on the receiving end of desperate gobbling.

When this disharmony occurs one partner can feel rejected while the other feels resentful. A few standing rules will help while you are phasing into harmony. First, when you're feeling needy, give. Do something genuinely selfless for your partner or someone else. Your energy needs to flow outward to restore a sense of well-being. Second, at any time, either of you must be free to ask for a few moments of hugging, or gentle stroking (at the discretion of the giver) and be sure of receiving them. Of course, the giving partner can give as much as he or she is inclined to give (within the bounds of this *Phase* of the *Exchanges*). Third, whoever is asking for affection must cheerfully soak up the giver's gift, even if it is only the few minimum hugs. If you are receiving, do not push for more. Focus instead on your love for your partner and think of ways you can express your love that would comfort and relax your partner instead of focusing on what would feel best to you.

Enjoy the glow from not exhausting your desire. Because of that glow you will always welcome union. If deprivation haunts you, focus on your gratitude for having a partner. Remind yourself that you have the power to heal *if you give*, and if necessary, meditate, pray or simply take a few deep breaths and release them slowly. Never try to take more, especially under the guise of making "gifts" of sexual stimulation to your partner. Manipulative behavior, or taking under the pretense of giving, is energetically draining. Even if you both stay loving, you cannot build up the solid core of mutual energy needed to find true satisfaction.

Above all, be patient. With consistent generosity any uneasiness will gradually lose its urgency (provided both of you also avoid genital orgasm). Your subconscious and brain chemistry will catch up with the fact that you are no longer starving for affection—or being repeatedly "devoured." Try these rules for a couple weeks before making any judgments about your sexual compatibility.

Humanity is starved for affectionate touch with no strings attached. It's the strings, after all, that have caused male and female to cut off the natural, nourishing flow of energy between them. You both need to rediscover there is an endless supply of welcome, generous contact between you that increases the pleasure for you both when it takes the form of mutual gifts of affection.

Before beginning the *Activity*, talk about what you experienced following the previous *Exchange*. Are you having trouble sleeping together? If so, experience has shown that it is best *not* to give in to the urge to separate. Just enjoy your nights together and try to catch a nap at some other point in the day. Eventually your body will adjust to your new intention to let nothing stand between you and healthy intimacy. Could you feel differences between giving and grabbing in your hugs? In your partner's hugs? Did it feel good to give even if you were sleepy? Do you feel happy? If you do, tell your partner why.

Suggested Preparation

Sounds: Beautiful, peaceful music in the background.

Time Out: She should lie, face up, with her head near him. He should cradle her head in his hands, with his palms resting on the surface beneath her head, and be still for about 5 minutes. She should just take deep breaths, as he sends her loving energy through his hands.

Watch Dog: For this *Exchange*, **he** is the Dog.

152

Attire: Comfortable shirts and comfortable shorts or modest underwear.

ACTIVITY

- Too often words create distance or superficiality, not deeper intimacy. So let silence reign. Use eyes, smiles, touches and flowing, unseen energy to communicate instead.

- Sit next to your partner on the bed, as he or she lies next to you. Take turns touching your partner with the goal of communicating how much you cherish him/her. Imagine that there are rays of radiant energy coming out of your hands. This powerful energy heals your lover and strengthens both your energy fields as it is exchanged. Make it a habit to touch your partner only when this energy is streaming from your hands. That way you can be sure you are always in *give* mode.

- Now try sending loving, sexual energy up through your heart and streaming out through your hands. What does it feel like to think of sexual energy as something you give? As something you nourish another with?

- Little kisses of faces, necks, covered areas, arms, and legs are fine, but avoid intentional stimulation of your partner's genitals and rubbing your genitals on your partner. And for this *Exchange* also avoid tongue kissing. Relax.

- When you are being touched, remain passive and just enjoy being nurtured. Feel your partner's love, warmth and energy flowing into you. Do not tell your partner what to do (unless you are over stimulated and need to halt); let him/her surprise you.

THE SNUGGLE

- Relax in each other's arms in a comfortable position. If you try spoon position again, whoever is on the outside can place his/her hand on the other's chest over any clothing. If he is feeling over-stimulated, she can rest her hand lovingly on his penis over his clothes as she holds him in spoon position.

- At night, if you awaken, ask your partner, with a touch, to hold you. And if asked, hold your partner—despite your sleepiness. Remember: the key to healing the unwelcome hunger we've all been trying to cope with is, "all you can eat" of selfless, loving touch—not geared toward satisfying your own sexual hunger. Instead use your desire to send healing energy streaming into your partner.

NOTE: You will need pencils and paper for the next *Exchange*.

Exchange 3
USE 'EM AND YOU LOSE 'EM

Whom do you value most in your life (other than your partner)? Usually it's someone you are devoted to. That is, it's someone whose welfare you often place before your own. You probably think that's because the one you adore is especially deserving of your selfless attention. They are—but so is your lover.

So don't be fooled by appearances. The fact is, you control your image of others, regardless of the shape they're in at any given moment. When you look at another from a space of caring, appreciation, adoration or desire to nurture, you see a reflection of your own open heart. That gives the object of your affection a glow that appears to be missing from people you don't care for in this way.

Unfortunately, we tend to bestow this selfless vision only upon those whom we perceive as being safe to love (like a child, a pet or a spiritual teacher). And thanks to years of alienation between the sexes (born of the fallout from conventional sex) we seldom feel a sexual partner is totally safe to love. Instead we view the opposite sex through a haze of defensiveness. This causes us to undervalue our sexual partners shortly after we begin having sex with them. Therefore we seldom attain the degree of mutual, openhearted reverence necessary to reap the full benefits of intimacy.

It's very difficult to see our error because our body chemistry makes us feel we have reason to be defensive. The alternative is to choose emotions that open the energy field around the heart, such as caring, appreciation, devotion and so on. As we saw in Chapter 3, we then produce the hormone, oxytocin, which governs our desire to bond deeply with another and to nurture selflessly.

Value the golden opportunity before you. Understand that your physical well-being, your ability to experience wholeness, and your spiritual vision are all at stake in each intimate encounter. Raise your sights, because when you see the inner beauty in your partner you will begin to grasp your own.

Before beginning the *Activity*, talk about what you experienced following the previous *Exchange*. Are you able to ask for the comfort you want without insisting on your former agenda for intimate encounters? Are you able to let your partner sleep between rounds of affection? Or are you bent on getting what you want? Protect your partner's sense of safety and well-being. Do you feel at ease? Do you feel grateful? Are you feeling less sexually frustrated than you thought you would? Take a moment right now to think of something nice you could do for your partner in the next 24 hours. Surprise him or her.

Whoops! Did someone have an orgasm? If so, refer to the "FOUL WEATHER WARNING" in the introduction to the first *Phase*.

Suggested Preparation

Materials: Pencils and paper.

Sounds: Beautiful, peaceful music in the background.

Time Out: He should lie, face up, with his head near her. She should cradle his head in her hands, with her palms resting on the surface beneath his head, and be still for about 5 minutes. He should just take deep breaths as she sends him loving energy through her hands.

Watch Dog: For this *Exchange*, **she** is the Dog.

Attire: Comfortable shirts and comfortable shorts or modest underwear.

156

ACTIVITY

- First, think of someone in your life whom you value (or have valued) very highly. Take a few moments to *feel* the feelings of adoration you have (or had). See if you can consciously transfer those feelings onto your partner. Does your heart open or close? Notice the difference, if any, between the selfless feelings your have for the one you adore and your affection for your partner. (There is no need to share with your partner the identity of the person or pet you are thinking of, although you certainly may.)

- Now, take a few minutes to write down at least three things you appreciate about your partner that the one whom you thought of does not add to your life. Maybe it's his or her wacky sense of humor, warm hugs or sunny smile.

- Express your gratitude to your partner for his or her gifts with a hug or other touch. Share what you have written.

THE SNUGGLE

- Relax. Now, snuggle each other as long as you like. Avoid intentional stimulation of your partner's genitals and rubbing your genitals on your partner. If you choose to tongue kiss, imagine that your partner's lips are the lips of his or her heart. Be gentle, not arousing.

- Take frequent breaks from kissing to breathe, smile and relax.

Exchange 4
ADDICTION

When you think of a scantily clad person of the opposite sex willingly lying next to you does a "cookie jar" mentality steal over you? That is, do you suddenly have the urge to grab what cookies you can and wolf 'em down before this seeming window of opportunity slams shut? Whoa, Baby!

When it comes to intimate encounters most of us have developed unconscious routines geared toward the goals of conventional sex. Because the payoff is powerful (rapid or noisy climaxes for ourselves or our partner, accompanied by brain chemical buzzes that feel great—until their hangover kicks in) these routines can be as tenacious as a substance addiction.

Some routines cause us to behave so predictably that we don't even think about what we're doing. We may then mistake our robot-like behavior for spontaneity. Even when we are conscious of our behavior we may "mentalize" sex, carefully orchestrating each step. Such habits get in the way of mastering this new approach.

Your new goal cannot be reached by intellect, blind passion or force of will. It's a state of mind you relax into and it's the product of two comfortable, open hearts. The *Snuggles* in the *Exchanges* can help because they are entirely inconsistent with former routines. They're built around the principles of no demands, no expectations and no pressure to perform. Basically they are about **not** doing. This permits an entirely new body chemistry to accompany your lovemaking. The inevitable exchange will do the rest.

When you first experiment with an approach to intimacy that doesn't feed your sexual addiction you may occasionally find you feel disoriented, irritable, stubbornly resistant—or totally at a loss. When such feelings arise try not to identify with them as "your will." They are the will of your primitive brain. So don't rationalize falling back into your addiction on the theory that you simply want to please your partner, you have sensual needs that aren't being met, or you'll never again feel any pleasure if you can't produce your passion body chemicals.

Realize that, thanks to your former programming, you are just like any other addict: you want your fix and withdrawal is a discomfort you'd rather avoid. Addiction creates a powerful urge to cling to your old habit—with its predictable "reward"—whatever the cost. In this case indulging your addiction is guaranteed to isolate you on some level, and cheat you of the greatest benefits of intimacy.

The good news is that while you are doing the *Exchanges* you have a way to ease your withdrawal: you have someone to love. If you can focus on your love and gratitude for your partner, and on making it safe for your partner to open to you completely, your heart will produce oxytocin and charge up its electromagnetic field. That makes possible a true sense of oneness. Every step in this direction feels so good, and enables you to feel the love coming from your partner so powerfully, that you can drop your passion addiction *almost* painlessly.

As you learn to stay in your heart your genitals will surprise you by aligning with your new intention—they'll be ready for action without any conscious foreplay. So trust the process and don't yield to self-destructive impulses. Passion-based body chemistry ultimately makes you both defensive.

Tip: Be especially careful of morning erections. They tend to *not* to be heart centered. If you cuddle in the morning, begin with a "Time Out" head hold or gently rub your partner over his/her heart, or sit up and meditate together.

Before beginning the *Activity*, talk about the previous *Exchange*. Take out the lists you made last time. Do you have anything to add that you are grateful to your partner for? Did you find that the things you valued most in your partner were related to sexual gratification or your other personal material plane agendas? If so, recognize that you are

159

denying yourself the most precious gift your partner has for you: an open heart. Did you remember to do something nice as a surprise for your partner? Do you feel satisfied?

Whoops! Did someone have an orgasm? If so, refer to the "FOUL WEATHER WARNING" in the introduction to the first *Phase*.

Suggested Preparation

Sounds: Beautiful, peaceful music in the background.

Materials: A chair.

Time Out: Sit facing each other and take a couple minutes to do an *"Energy Circulation"* (see introduction to this *Phase*). Join hands for a moment and look into each other's eyes.

Watch Dog: For this *Exchange*, **he** is the Dog.

Attire: Comfortable shirts and comfortable shorts or modest underwear.

ACTIVITY

• Partner A, lie comfortably on your stomach, on a mat on the floor, with hands palms down near your head. Be prepared to let your lover know what feels good with wordless sounds and sighs.

• B, stand next to A and use your bare *foot* to massage A gently, consciously sending loving energy through your foot. Begin by placing your foot on one of A's hands. Gently rock some of your weight onto it. Repeat, slowly moving up the fleshy part of A's arms to where the shoulders and neck connect, and then across the shoulders. Then travel around A's body, using the chair to balance yourself as needed. Remember to stand on the soles of A's feet for a moment, too.

160

- Experiment with a gentle rocking motion that allows A to exhale as your weight descends. And hold the pressure gently but firmly when you feel (or hear) your partner requesting more. You can increase the weight you put on A as A relaxes. Focus on fleshy parts, avoiding the head, spine, shins, elbows and knees.

- Switch roles.

THE SNUGGLE

- Selflessly, safely snuggle each other for as long as you like.

- When it's time to go to sleep, remember, keep it simple. If you choose to kiss with open mouths, take breaks and do not use your kisses to heat your partner up. Give.

Suggested
Time: At least 15 minutes per partner.

Exchange 5
HIGHER LOVE

Are you adjusting to being "on" all the time? You may find you long for an energy crash to bring your level of sexual arousal back to "normal." Or you may seek to deaden yourself with television, pulp fiction, recreational drugs or alcohol. Yet, remember, the goal of the *Exchanges* is to tap into higher levels of energy that will also feel normal as we grow accustomed to them. Make an effort to enjoy your higher frequency instead of undermining it. Any discomfort will pass if you give any surplus energy to others while you stabilize.

Remind yourself that the urge to drop your energy is not benign. It's your biological death reflex. Give life a try for a few weeks. Meanwhile, use energy surges to go beyond your old limitations: paint a room, discover your life's purpose, help a friend, take a walk in nature, write a book or a song, or tackle something you've been procrastinating about.

And if the energy still feels like too much, find a way to give it to your partner. Rub his feet, scratch her back, help with a chore. It will make the adjustment to your higher voltage bearable and energize your partner as well—which will pay big dividends during your more intimate moments. Even if your partner isn't around, cook a favorite dish, repair or sew something, plan an adventure for the two of you. In short befriend your sexual arousal. Use it as a signal that it's time to give.

Often your newfound energy will seek to express itself as a passion stampede. You may feel like you have so much energy that you'll never again feel depleted. Be ready for this biological deception. It's an urge to go over Niagara Falls in a barrel.

While you're still stabilizing, any rush will likely be followed by a lull. If so, relax and trust that when your energy comes up again, it will be more centered. Remember that you may also ask your partner for more loving attention—as often as necessary.

162

Before beginning the next *Exchange*, talk about what you experienced following the previous *Exchange*. Were you able to relax deeply? Did it feel good to be stepped on? Did you find it effortless to give a deep massage this way? Do you feel pampered? Is either of you thrusting or writhing on top of the other while cuddling? (If so, hold off on that.) If male, are you noticing that your burning desire to ejaculate is less than you expected?

Whoops! Did someone have an orgasm? If so, refer to the "FOUL WEATHER WARNING" in the introduction to the first *Phase*.

Suggested Preparation

Sounds: Beautiful, peaceful music in the background.

Time Out: She should lie, face up, with her head near him. He should cradle her head in his hands, with his palms resting on the surface beneath her head, and be still for about 5 minutes. She should just take deep breaths as he sends her loving energy through his hands.

Watch Dog: For this *Exchange*, **she** is the Dog.

Attire: Comfortable shirts and comfortable shorts or modest underwear.

ACTIVITY

- Partner B lays his/her head in A's lap. A lovingly rubs B's head while repeating the following phrases with as many endings as he/she can come up with. B quietly enjoys the head rub.

   "I feel funny doing these *Exchanges* because…"

   "Some of the things I like about my time with you are…"

163

- Switch roles.

- Now, each of you should demonstrate a type of touching that is soothing to you but not directly sexually arousing. Practice comforting each other using this customized touch. As you go forward with the *Exchanges*, use your partner's favorite touch frequently, even without waiting for a request.

THE SNUGGLE

- Safely snuggle each other for as long as you like.

- When it's time to go to sleep, remember: no intentional stimulation of your partner's genitals, or rubbing your genitals on your partner. Just reverent touch and heartfelt kisses.

- If you awaken in the night, ask your partner, with a touch, to hold you for a moment or two. And if asked, do it—despite your sleepiness.

Exchange 6
LISTENING

Enduring, nourishing, sane harmony between the sexes is not only possible, but also natural—once you learn to shift your body chemistry from passion to the chemistry of deep bonding. But there appears to be no middle ground between these two chemistries. This is why you want to steer consistently for selfless feelings in the bedroom. Forgiveness, too, opens the heart, creating a feeling of safety, and encouraging a beneficial relaxation response at a body chemistry level.

So in this *Exchange* do some emotional housecleaning and forgiving. Your quarry is not a spectral warrior who stabbed you in a past life. It's any guilt you may be harboring from your own misguided actions in this lifetime. Bold adventurers that you are, you have spent time on a planet where love and fear are so painfully entangled that it's been impossible to get it right up till now. Out of balance, undernourished at an energy level—and just plain cantankerous sometimes as a natural result—you've hurt others or played the martyr. And probably both. Like everyone else, you've had moments where you were less than honest, brutally sharp of tongue, uncontrollably addicted to something, compulsively over-controlling, hurtfully suspicious without cause, or appallingly greedy or self-centered.

It's time to accept that you've had very little choice to date. And to recognize that those who hurt or offended you had equally little choice—no matter how it seemed. Why? Because they've also been feeling uneasy. Even martyrs, addicts and other victims have ultimately drawn to themselves their painful experiences due to feelings of vulnerability. Feeling deprived, we experience intense hormone fluctuations that attract to us, or seem to justify, even the worst behavior. Without the comfort of wholeness we've all contributed to the general chaos.

One way to exorcise your guilt ghosts is to get them off your chest. Share them with a listener who now understands everyone's absolute innocence—your partner. Trust is a vital aspect of true intimacy.

165

Discover that your innocence is precious to your lover. He/she would not have you suffer another pang of guilt. The past is over. The only time you can move toward inner wholeness is right now—and you can do it together.

So, bare your soul instead of your body, and release each other from the harsh sentences of the past. *Anything revealed is off limits for future discussion without the permission of the one who shares it.* Just hold each other and talk.

Before beginning the *Activity*, talk about what you experienced following the previous *Exchange*. Have you noticed any shifts in the way you feel about each other since you've been doing the *Exchanges*? Do you feel your partner cares deeply for you? Is either of you reaching in the other's underwear while snuggling? (If so, hold off on that.) When you awaken your partner for a hug, do you try to grab even more than you are given? In the morning, do you touch each other's hearts or meditate before you move on to other types of touch? Have you discussed whether you need to test for venereal disease? If you do need to test now is the time. How has your pace been? Are you likely to complete the first 14 *Exchanges* before the suggested four-week period is up? If not, pick up the pace.

Whoops! Did someone have an orgasm? If so, refer to the "FOUL WEATHER WARNING" in the introduction to the first *Phase*.

Suggested Preparation

Sounds: Beautiful, peaceful music in the background.

Time Out: He should lie, face up, with his head near her. She should cradle his head in her hands, with her palms resting on the surface beneath his head, and be still for about 5 minutes. He should just take deep breaths as she sends him loving energy through her hands.

Watch Dog: For this *Exchange*, **he** is the Dog.

Attire: Comfortable shirts and comfortable shorts or modest underwear.

ACTIVITY

- Choose a position. Either:
  - Sit comfortably, facing each other and holding each other's hands, or
  - Partner B, lie down with your head on a pillow, on Partner A's lap.

- Partner A, listen to B talk, giving him/her your full attention. Express your empathy through your eyes, or hands on B's head. But do not react to what is being said with gestures, nods, head shaking, smiles, frowns or other actions that evaluate your partner's remarks or delivery. Just be there.

- B, choose one of the topics from below, and talk about your feelings relating to it for 10 minutes. Do not ask for any feedback. Just talk.

  - Your least noble action with respect to the opposite sex. Was it infidelity, emotional blackmail, insisting on having a child over your partner's objections, abandonment, sexual aggression? (Never mind what they did to you.)

  - Anything you want/need to get off your chest (addictions, herpes, prescription antidepressants you are taking, or whatever).

- When your partner finishes, look into his/her eyes and deliver this message in your own words: "You are completely innocent. These are just leftover symptoms from years on a planet that has been governed by painful separation. The past is over. We can heal best

167

by strengthening each other." Then, hold each other silently for as long as you like.

- Change roles.

Tomorrow, and thereafter, feel free to confess any other demons that pop up. Just listen without judging when your lover is talking. Comfort him/her without words. And talk about your demons, too.

· THE SNUGGLE

- Snuggle each other reverently for as long as you like.

- When it's time to go to sleep, remember, just reverent touch and loving kisses.

NOTE: You will need a cassette tape or CD player and some music for the next *Exchange*.

Exchange 7
MUSICAL INTERLUDE

In the past you've used your primitive brain's plan of arousal and release as a way to manage your sexual desire. In effect, you managed it by killing it temporarily with a conventional orgasm. Now you're learning another way to manage sexual desire. Instead of an addictive dopamine rush followed by a subconscious sense of deprivation, you are moving toward never-ending waves. That is, you allow your sexual energy to pull you closer to your partner and then deliberately calm yourself (by circulating your energy as you contract your uro-genital muscles, if necessary). You lapse back into a resting state. You may be astonished to discover that once you are calm again you do not feel in the least unsatisfied. Better yet, you have the desire and energy to begin another cycle of exhilarating union.

In this *Exchange*, experiment with this cyclical approach to loving using music, exercise, dance and stillness. Even those who hate dancing have enjoyed this *Exchange*. So try it as written despite any reservations.

Before beginning the *Activity*, talk about what you experienced following the previous *Exchange*. Were you completely open and honest yourself no matter how dirty your linen? Did you think of something later that you wish you had said? Go ahead. Did you find it easy not to judge your lover harshly? Do you see that there are no reliable degrees of wrongness? That is, that insane behavior of any kind is inevitable and forgivable while love and fear are confused—and humanity is unwittingly using its sexual energy to trigger defensiveness that distorts judgment and causes us to make errors? Do you feel lighter today? Do you feel cherished?

Whoops! Did someone have an orgasm? If so, refer to the "FOUL WEATHER WARNING" in the introduction to the first *Phase*.

Suggested Preparation

Sounds: One of you chooses one or two sexy, rhythmic songs. The other chooses one or two slower, inspiringly romantic songs. And one of you chooses some peaceful, meditative instrumental music.

Time Out: Sit facing each other and take a couple minutes to do an "*Energy Circulation*" (see introduction to the first *Phase*). Join hands for a moment and look into each other's eyes.

Watch Dog: For this *Exchange*, **she** is the Dog.

Attire: For the *Snuggle,* comfortable shirts and shorts or modest underwear.

ACTIVITY

• Put on the energetic music. Either use it to do rigorous exercise or just dance in whatever way the music moves you. Be as sexy as you like. Experiment with belly dancing, African and Caribbean moves, if so inspired.

• When you're exhausted put on the romantic music and dance in each other's arms. Just swaying back and forth to the music is fine if formal dance steps are not in your repertoire. Kiss as romantically as you like, but keep it reverent—not hungry. Imagine you're making love to your partner as you dance but don't directly stimulate each other's genitals.

• Dance for at least 20 minutes (including both the rapid and romantic music). But take seated time-outs to circulate energy together if the Watch Dog advises it.

- Now, put on meditative music. Lie on your backs and place the hand nearest your lover over his or her genitals. Without moving your hand, send loving energy into your lover through your hand with each out breath. Imagine it returning through your lover's hand with each in breath. Relax completely.

THE SNUGGLE

- Kiss and snuggle each other for as long as you like.

- Tonight, when you're ready to fall asleep, lie together in spoon position for a while.

NOTE: **You will need pencils and paper and massage oil for tomorrow's** *Exchange* **and for some of the** *Exchanges* **that follow.**

Exchange 8
LIMITLESS UNION

One block to spiritual union between you and your partner is the subtle belief that your spiritual path is different. The experience of oneness between male and female need not conflict with any path; it is merely the rediscovery of the joint potential that lies in all of us regardless of doctrine. But you may be setting yourself up for failure when you attempt this type of sacred union as a path to heightened awareness if you've practiced Transcendental Meditation for years, obeyed the dictates of various external authorities on *A Course in Miracles*, or followed any of countless masters teaching spiritual-sounding ego autonomy in one form or another.

You may be convinced that you (or your external authority) have found the way to God without overcoming the alienation between male and female. And that anything to do with sexual relationships is a sideline. At best you see it as a pastime that hopefully won't detract from your real spiritual work. Perhaps it's a way to manage your sexual energy so as to avoid the energy drop from masturbation. At worst, sexual union is a cause for intense guilt. Attitudes like this can lead to carelessness, lack of focus or self-sabotage—the blame for which will be projected onto your partner. Worse yet, when these attitudes do cause problems you will retreat into spiritual elitism to comfort yourself. "Ah, I knew all along that spiritual sexuality was a red herring," you'll confidently say to yourself as you settle back into emotional separation with your preferred brand of spiritual chicken soup before you.

Yet, has your interpretation of your spiritual path made celibacy (without masturbation) a viable alternative for you? Has it made your relationships, however holy, a source of peace? Or has it just made it easier for you to forgive the seemingly inevitable friction and separation? Has your path led you to a sense of creative, productive giving? Or does it merely let you bliss out while you try to stay comfortable in your own, isolated mental space, ideally without demanding too much from others?

172

If you recognize that celibacy is not working for you, that your relationships continue in emotional turmoil, or that you are stuck in unproductive denial or stagnation, then it may be time to give the spiritual reunion of male and female an enthusiastic try. You can always return your sole allegiance to your current approach later.

For now, use your connection with the Divine to ask whether sacred union is the Divine's will for you. And if the answer is "yes," then set aside all preconceptions and sage advice to the contrary. Reach for this method of circumventing the ego with the full force of your will. The results may delight you—and your Creator.

Before beginning the *Activity*, talk about what you experienced following the previous *Exchange*. What was your favorite phase of the musical *Exchange*? Did you allow yourself to calm down after the romantic dancing? Do you feel you are being nurtured in your relationship? Are you spending every night together? If not, don't go forward with the *Exchanges*. You're trying to go too fast. If you've had an argument, have you tried lying together without words, in spoon position, before attempting to resolve your differences?

Whoops! Did someone have an orgasm? If so, refer to the "FOUL WEATHER WARNING" in the introduction to the first *Phase*.

Suggested Preparation

Sounds: Beautiful, peaceful music in the background.

Materials: Pencil and paper. Massage oil.

Time Out: Each of you writes down any unexpected benefits or happy coincidences that have flowed from your connection with your partner. Share them with each other. Do you sense the Divine trying to nourish you through your relationship? If so, are you showing your gratitude by nurturing your partner?

173

Watch Dog: For this *Exchange*, **he** is the Dog.

Attire: Comfortable shirts and comfortable shorts or modest underwear.

ACTIVITY

- Partner A is the massage therapist, B the recipient. B, lie comfortably with your head on a towel and pillow in A's lap, feet facing away from A's front side.

- A, before beginning, energize your hands by moving them apart and then slowly together until they are almost touching. Repeat this motion and feel the energy build up between you hands. Meanwhile, B, clench your teeth, scrunch your face toward the tip of your nose in a tight ball, and hold it for at least ten counts before relaxing completely.

- A, put a drop of massage oil on your hands. Rub B's cheeks, nose and forehead gently up toward you and out to the side, using movements that would feel good to you. Allow your love for B to flow through your hands. B, visualize your mask melting away, revealing your true, much loved, self.

- Now, A, gently rub the rims of B's ears between your fingers and then tug on them, and on B's earlobes, slowly and firmly. Next, rub B's temples with a gentle, circular motion. Knead B's scalp and the base of B's skull. Conclude by gently, but firmly, pressing the top of B's skull for a count of three. Ask B what else he/she would like.

- Change roles.

THE SNUGGLE

- Kiss and snuggle each other for as long as you like. Can you feel caring energy flowing out through your hands and arms as you touch each other?

- Tomorrow indulge in mini-shoulder rubs and kisses, whenever possible.

Suggested
Time: At least 15 minutes per partner for the massage.

Exchange 9
THE HEART AND THE INTELLECT

The ancient wisdom of the Chinese Taoists, the Indian tantra practitioners, the earliest Christians (as revealed by the Gnostic Gospels), and even Plato, suggest that behind the illusion of separate male and female egos there is only one cosmic being, pulsating with current. That current flows between two poles, one "male" and one "female." The two poles are not separate—indeed their union is so dynamic and powerful that its potential is beyond our current ability to imagine for as long as we feel separate.

Fortunately we can teach ourselves to experience that power by safely charging each other up to new levels of perception that allow us to perceive our oneness. As we make it safe to love our hearts begin to generate powerful electromagnetic fields that extend our perception beyond the physical, and synchronize easily with other open hearts. When in synch we may feel like we are uniting beyond the body. We taste union with that ultimate cosmic "male/femaleness." These glimpses furnish a sense of wholeness and well-being so profound that our entire self image shifts away from the mundane. We feel we've entered another realm.

In fact we've just expanded into a realm that was always there, and merely veiled by our self-induced defensiveness. Unfortunately, the hangover from conventional sex has kept us out of synch and left us feeling helplessly, hopelessly separate and utterly ordinary. To be sure, we can't change a sense of separateness to a sense of oneness by force of will. And yet, the wisdom of the heart is not alone sufficient to restore us to oneness. We still need force of will, or intellect, to make sound choices:

• We consciously choose sexual behavior that will decrease our defensiveness by avoiding the passion trigger. As one book puts it, "remove the barriers to love and union occurs naturally."

176

- While we heal, we choose not to separate in response to any leftover defensive emotional patterns.

As explained in Chapter 5, our subconscious has the capacity to remember emotional patterns and respond with neurochemicals that cause us to react even before our intellect has a chance to select the best response. Unfortunately years of disharmony between the sexes has left most of us with a powerful baseline emotional response of uneasy separation in the face of intimacy. Separation feels safer even though it actually damages our health and lowers our expectations. If we act on this subconscious urge to separate it harms our relationships.

If instead we stay close, refuse to create space for ourselves, and nurture each other, any urge to separate passes in a matter of days. Eventually the unmistakable benefits of this new approach to sex teach us a new intimacy baseline—one that welcomes life enhancing closeness.

Before beginning the *Activity*, talk about what you experienced following the previous *Exchange*. Did you enjoy your face massages? What do you like most about your time together? Is your "horniness" less uncomfortable than you imagined it would be? Is your need for space less than you imagined it would be?

Whoops! Did someone have an orgasm? If so, refer to the "FOUL WEATHER WARNING" in the introduction to the first *Phase*.

Suggested Preparation

Sounds: Rhythmic music, followed by beautiful, peaceful music.

Materials: Pencils and paper.

Mood Setting: Many cultures on the planet still make love for hours using lazy, almost imperceptible, hip circles in mutually comfortable positions. In fact, making love by thrusting on top of a female partner was deemed so foreign by

177

some civilizations that it was branded "the missionary position." How did the missionaries get it so wrong? Well, thrusting is the fastest way to fertilization. As the Church taught that procreation was the only acceptable use of sexual attraction, it's no wonder much of the West acquired this emotionally alienating habit.

So take a moment to remind your hips how to move without thrusting. Dance. Put on some rhythmic music. Begin by standing, facing each other, hands on hips. Now, pretend you are doing the hula. Bend your knees slightly and circle your hips to the right a few times. Change direction. Experiment with slower circles. With smaller circles. Do this for at least one song, or a few minutes. Try holding each other's hips while you do it.

Watch Dog: For this *Exchange*, **she** is the Dog.

Attire: Comfortable shirts and comfortable shorts or modest underwear.

ACTIVITY

- Play detective. Suppose it were possible to experience your ego dissolving into an experience of cosmic unity with your partner…right now. Draw the following:

How do I *really* feel about merging?	
I'd be afraid of…	*The good things would be…*

Any uneasy feelings go in the first column. Don't make yourself wrong for any anxiety you feel—just get in touch with your reservations and do your best to describe them honestly. Any feelings of enthusiasm for closer union go in the second column.

- When you have both finished examine your fears. Accept that uneasiness will naturally haunt you until you learn to keep your hearts open. Yet, even now, you don't have to believe in your fears. Be suspicious of their validity. Are they supported by any current proof? Or are they based on vague emotional "what if's" and past hurts—sustained when conventional sex or masturbation were still in the picture? Could your fears indeed be an old baseline pattern adversely affecting your ability to open your heart in the present?

- Write affirmations that will help you release your old programming. For example, if you feel like merging would be a dangerously emotionally intense experience, you might affirm, "An experience of merging is natural and allows me to feel more loved." Write an affirmation for each fear. Turn to them when these old patterns haunt you.

- Next turn to the "happy anticipation" list. Take a moment to feel what true union would be like. Can you feel tingling? Expansion? Write down exactly what you feel when you imagine merging. How does the area around your heart feel?

- Share your findings with your partner.

THE SNUGGLE

Hold each other comfortably, sitting up, if possible. Silently visualize the electromagnetic fields around your hearts getting larger and more powerful. Feel yours pulsing with a loving rhythm. Imagine it coming into synchronization with the rhythm of your partner's heart field. Feel your heart producing the hormones that help you bond deeply with another.

Exchange 10
FOOT LOVE

It's time to go even deeper emotionally. Though you probably harbor the ideal that your erotic and loving energy flow in tandem, in practice you may well unwittingly separate the two. Perhaps you stay loving but very little sexual current flows. Or perhaps you go for the stimulation only to find that the tenderness you felt in quieter moments swiftly evaporates.

Any gap between heart and genitals is merely the defensive mechanism, or "Intimacy Sabotaging Device" (Chapter 5) that protects you from ongoing intimacy. Why? Because immersion in each other is artificially linked in your subconscious with fear, panic, scarcity, punishment and even death. "The wages of sin (sexual expression) *have* been death." Death of feelings of ecstasy, death from wasting illnesses born of broken hearts or guilt for past actions, death from self-destructive actions, and death of belief in an unconditionally loving Creator. In short, mankind has been pursuing fulfillment through habits that doomed it to lifeless or broken relationships, physical deterioration, and spiritual stagnation.

Intimacy without fear rejuvenates you, heightens awareness and can ultimately shift your perception to higher ground. At a profound level you know this. It's the deeper reason you have been trying to fall in love all your life. Of course, until now, your biological programming has taken over every time you fell in love and steered you right toward uneasy separation. Or you have evaded physical intimacy, thus preventing total surrender in a shared experience.

Above all, only recently have you considered whether there was a third option that would allow mutual surrender and merging in a cocoon of safety. Habit speaks with a very loud voice. It takes an independent mind to experiment with the radical approach of healing old fears through regular, intimate contact without letting biology direct the proceedings.

180

Play with expressing your desire for each other through your eyes and words. As you draw your sexual desire up and surround it with heart energy, it will ultimately express itself even more powerfully—in truly inspired ways.

Before beginning the *Activity*, talk about what you experienced following the previous *Exchange*. Are you spoiling each other with thoughtful gestures and gifts? Is one of you giving more than the other? If so, the one giving less should try to give more so the flow is more balanced. Do you find it easier and easier to relax after each wave of sexual arousal? Do you feel more confident? Do you find you're more open to other people? Do you feel more powerfully male if you're a man? More like relaxing into the role of "boat" if you're a woman (leaving the man to pilot you safely)? How is your heart feeling right now?

Whoops! Did someone have an orgasm? If so, refer to the "FOUL WEATHER WARNING" in the introduction to the first *Phase*.

Suggested Preparation

Sounds: Beautiful, peaceful music.

Materials: Massage oil and towels. Fill the tub, or a dishpan with warm, slightly soapy water.

Mood Setting: Sit close to each other and look into one another's eyes for one minute.

Watch Dog: For this *Exchange*, **he** is the Dog.

Attire: Comfortable shirts (except during massage) and comfortable shorts or modest underwear.

ACTIVITY

- If possible, soak your feet together in the tub or a dishpan. If not, take turns. After 10 minutes, tenderly dry each other's feet thoroughly and give each foot a kiss. Exchange foot massages.

- The recipient's feet should ideally be at the level of your chest, with legs relaxed and comfortably supported. Now, energize your hands by clapping or rubbing them for 10 seconds, and then resting them for a moment, palms up. Sense the heat or tingling in them.

- Place the feet on a towel and rub them gently with massage oil. Allow your love to flow through your hands as you massage your lover's feet silently, using your thumbs to press as deeply and firmly as you can without causing pain. Knead each bit of surface area of the sole, penetrating deep below the skin. Then give special attention to the following:

- The pituitary stimulation point in the middle of each big toe pad.

- The pineal stimulation point, up from the pituitary point and slightly toward the inside of the foot.

- The sexual balancing points (the heel, the areas just below the ankle on both sides of the foot, and the Achilles tendon area, just above the heel). Use circular movements of the thumb and forefinger.

THE SNUGGLE

Kiss and snuggle each other for as long as you like. Take turns putting your hands over each other's hearts. Consciously send your partner your healing energy for specific purposes, such as, to "heal his sore ankle," to "help her through her annual review at work," to "break through an old defense," to "release an addiction."

Exchange 11
FISH FOOD

Do you still sometimes feel like fish food spread before a hungry fish during your lovemaking? If you're the "fish" in this situation, recognize that the more you gobble the hungrier you'll feel over the next days. This happens because the flow of energy between you and your partner reflects taking and defensiveness rather than giving and openness. This behavior leads to addiction rather than peace of mind. Eventually this hunger will push you until you reach your primitive brain's unconscious, self-destructive goal: genital orgasm. And within two weeks the disharmony in your relationship will boggle your mind.

You've probably repeated this pattern in the past enough to recognize it. Yet, if you're still basing your intimacy on hunger, you're probably also blaming your partner for any dissatisfaction. To you, Dear Fish, it seems like all your problems would disappear if you only had a warmer, more loving partner.

You're right that you need a receptive partner. Yet it's up to you to reverse the flow of energy between you—thus creating a space in which your partner can safely open up. Think of yourself as a *supplier* instead of a *consumer*. Challenge yourself to bestow new forms of unselfish affection: massage your partner's hands, hug with no ulterior motive, give a head rub. Stop frequently, and look into your partner's eyes to reorient your intentions. Avoid veiled foreplay maneuvers masquerading as gifts. Though it may be counterintuitive, the more you selflessly nurture another, the more satisfied you'll feel.

If you're the "fish food," recognize that defensiveness is closing your heart at the moment. As a result, you, too, deliberately need to put your partner first. Be as warm and affectionate as possible and take the initiative so your partner unmistakably feels your love. Until the flow between you is corrected, confine yourself to non-sexual gifts of physical affection. You'll know when you feel like opening up more.

You may be surprised at how quickly the sparkles return to your intimacy. Meanwhile, be forgiving, and gently tell your partner if his or her behavior is "fishy." Voracious gobbling is not what it appears to be. It is not proof of sexiness or even desire for union with you. In fact, it is a defense to reunion, as it keeps everyone feeling very depleted and ordinary. It pushes you apart as effectively as your "cold fish" behavior.

Uneasiness has the effect of making us all feel like we have to look after "Number One," and we tend to make our decisions based what we imagine would be best for us. Sometimes that makes us grab; sometimes it makes us icy. Yet selfishness swiftly leads to isolation, making us feel even less nourished, more needy and more selfish. This is why the antidote to the separation virus is mutual giving.

Tips for "fish":

If you're feeling sexually frustrated use the energy circulation from the introduction to this *Phase* to regain your composure. It works.

When you're feeling the urge to gobble up your partner in the bedroom, understand that you are in suction mode energetically. You are draining your partner no matter how much physical pleasure you may dish out. You are not a safe lover. Stop and remind yourself that you want your partner always to feel safe enough to open completely in your arms. Touch his or her heart area with your palm. Focus on increasing the loving energy flowing out of your own heart and hand. Your actions will automatically shift as your intention changes.

Tips for "fish food":

Wordlessly demonstrate the kind of unselfish, affectionate lovemaking that makes you feel safe and open. Set the best possible example.
Be honest. Your partner may be having trouble distinguishing between heartfelt hugs and hungry hugs, but you know. Respond to the hungry ones with non-erotic, heartfelt affection and do not encourage a passion buildup.

184

Before beginning the *Activity,* **use this quiz to assess which roles you each habitually fall into.** Ignore the "A/P" boxes for the moment. *Only check a "HE" or "SHE" box if you both agree on who should check it.* Otherwise leave it blank.

During the *Exchanges,* which one of you has most often been:

	HE	A/P	SHE	A/P
1 Ready to get up and out of bed in the morning rather than cuddle?	☐		☐	
2 Crawling on top of the other, or asking your partner to crawl on top of you, despite instructions?	☐		☐	
3 Trying to reach in the other's clothing?	☐		☐	
4 Ready to stop snuggling and fall asleep?	☐		☐	
5 Asking for more touch?	☐		☐	
6 Suggesting your activities were growing too passionate?	☐		☐	

Now, whoever checked boxes 2, 3 or 5 should put an "A" in the appropriate column to the right of the boxes he or she checked. Whoever checked 1, 4, or 6, should put a "P" to the right of the boxes he or she checked. If you have more "A's" than "P's" in your column, you tend to be the "fishy" or *active* partner, and your partner is usually the "fish food" or *passive* partner.

Generally speaking, the active partner longs for more loving attention, and the passive partner needs to give more loving attention. For the next few *Exchanges,* switch roles. The active partner will consciously become the "Receiving Partner" (i.e., will take a more passive role). The more passive partner will deliberately take the active role and will be referred to as the "Giving Partner." This reversal of roles should help to balance the flow of energy between you. (If you could not decide who should check all the boxes, and so ended up in a tie, the man should take the passive, "Receiving Partner" role for the next few *Exchanges.*)

185

You may discover that these next *Exchanges* are your favorites. Often the partner who has been more active will find that he or she loves receiving more attention. And the partner who has been more passive realizes that he or she loves giving, as long as he or she is not feeling pushed.

After the next few *Exchanges* the man will take the giving role so she can fall into total receptivity. (She can still initiate affectionate attention, of course.) Her unguarded openness is actually the key to his gaining perfect control over the genital orgasm reflex—just as his increasing control will create a safe space in which she can open completely.

Whoops! Did someone have an orgasm? If so, refer to the "FOUL WEATHER WARNING" in the introduction to the first *Phase*.

Suggested Preparation

Sounds: Beautiful, peaceful music.

Mood Setting: She should sit facing him, close enough to hug. (If it is comfortable, try sitting in his lap on a chair.) Now, as you hug, breathe deeply, contracting your uro-genital muscles with each inhalation. Consciously send your energy from your heart into your partner's chest.

Watch Dog: For this *Exchange*, **she** is the Dog.

Attire: Comfortable shirts and comfortable shorts or modest underwear.

ACTIVITY

Sit facing each other and hum or tone together. Continue until you feel a powerful vibration in your forehead. Let it spread throughout your bodies. Keep it up for as long as you both can. Talk about how you feel afterward.

THE SNUGGLE

- Kiss and snuggle each other for as long as you like, trying out your new roles, as Giving and Receiving Partners.

- If it has been two weeks since either of you had a genital orgasm, try sleeping with your shirts off. Otherwise, she should continue to wear a shirt until two weeks are up. If shirts are off, take care not to fall back into classic foreplay. Keep all touch selfless and loving. If at any time, now, or in the future, she feels she is being "feasted upon" visually, she should replace her shirt.

NOTE: You will need to choose something inspiring to read to your partner for the next *Exchange*.

Exchange 12
MYSTERY OF STILLNESS

Have you tried touching each other over your hearts for a few moments when things start to heat up too rapidly? Have you tried holding each other in spoon if there's discord between you? If so, you've discovered how easy it is to restore harmony and a feeling of deep peace. You may also have discovered that powerful releases of old anxieties spontaneously occur in these periods of stillness.

Some years back psychologists did a study to determine what helps people permanently heal emotional trauma stored in their bodies. They had noticed that often people went through intense releases at workshops but didn't let go of the stored trauma. Instead, they often became "workshop junkies," repeatedly releasing, without really healing. The research found that the single factor that most often allowed fundamental healing was still, caring touch. With still touch, people could heal trauma, even without directly addressing the traumatic event. Apparently the sense of safety produced by conscious touch creates a space in which our bodies can release trauma for good.[48]

Many of us have unconsciously stored emotional trauma relating to sexual intimacy. Through conscious, healing touch we can assist our partners in releasing it permanently. In short, quiet, loving touch is a potent secret that we need to share with all those we love. When we simply change our state of mind in quiet shared stillness, seemingly insoluble problems attract solutions. Hopelessly hurt feelings give way to new perspectives. Together we are healing the sense of isolation and mistrust that are the roots of much emotional distress and old trauma. We literally change our inner states to "wholeness" simply by exchanging loving energy in stillness. Our external circumstances then naturally tend to align with that shift.

Before beginning the *Activity*, talk about what you experienced following the previous *Exchange*. Were you surprised at the power of the vibration you felt from the humming? Did you feel self-conscious?

188

Are you remembering to touch each other's hearts when you start caressing? Do you need to test for venereal disease? Are you likely to complete the first 14 *Exchanges* in four weeks from the time you began? Are you enjoying the *Activities*? Which was your favorite so far? What was it like to be the "Receiving Partner?" The "Giving Partner?"

Whoops! Did someone have an orgasm? If so, refer to the "FOUL WEATHER WARNING" in the introduction to the first *Phase*.

Suggested Preparation

Sounds: Beautiful, peaceful music.

Materials: 2 pens and some paper.

Mood Setting: Choose something inspiring to read to your partner. Take turns.

Watch Dog: For this *Exchange*, **he** is the Dog.

Attire: Comfortable shirts and shorts or modest underwear.

ACTIVITY

- Find the pens and paper. Now, each of you draws yourself in a powerful pose. Make it simple and don't worry about artistic merit. Around the image, write the best qualities you already have, qualities that you desire, and adjectives that describe the ideal you. Examples might be: *confidence, clarity, courage,* or *powerful, inspiring, joyful, loving* and so on. *Hint:* also think of some qualities you fault yourself for and add their opposites to the paper.

- Take about 10 minutes. When you've finished, exchange pictures with each other. Add to your partner's picture qualities he or she is already developing that you believe reflect his/her true inner radiance. Also add any wonderful qualities he/she may have

189

forgotten. Take care not to add qualities you wish your partner would develop—just support him or her in the changes he/she wishes to make. Compare.

THE SNUGGLE

Kiss and snuggle each other for as long as you like. The Giving Partner should take the lead, remember. If shirts are now off, be especially alert to avoid classic foreplay when you wake up. Keep caring energy flowing out through your hands and avoid deliberately heating each other up. Do not roll around on each other with shirts off.

NOTE: For the next *Exchange* you will need two light, comfortable blindfolds.

Exchange 13
HEIGHTENED SENSITIVITY

Strong, equal partners with no sense of lack most easily experience complete, totally satisfying, union. The kind of contact you've recently been engaging in, without peak orgasm, promotes that ideal sense of wholeness because it strengthens you both from the inside. But relationships have survived on mutual clutching and codependent weaknesses for a long time.

If you sense unequal behavior going on in your relationship admit it. Don't let your partner's loving reinforcement back you into always being the strong father for an infantile girl, or a giant nipple for a grasping baby boy. Decline the role of policeman or governess—or co-dependent cheerleader if your partner insists on clinging to an addiction. You can't always be the strong one or the one always required to prove your love to the satisfaction of your partner. And don't let your partner hook you with addictive lovemaking based on physical thrills. Such maneuvers reflect an unconscious death wish more than they reflect a healthy interest in sex. The *Exchanges* require two equal adults genuinely and generously seeking higher ends.

Be certain you're not rewarding unhealthy behavior just because it's accompanied by a heart-touching "I love you, Darling," a manipulative "You don't love me as much as I love you," or a curve ball like, "You always give yourself to me so completely" (as your partner pushes you past sound limits of behavior). Also be sure you aren't tolerating selfish behavior because your beloved manipulates you with, "You're an angel in my life," "I told you, you should be stricter with me," or "I'd like to give you more, but you always do all the giving." Nonsense. There are always creative ways to give. And if giving doesn't go both ways, it is draining.

Take care not to force your partner to choose between refusing to meet your imagined needs and yielding to dangerous behavior. This is a no-win situation. Your partner can never meet a need driven by your hungry behavior. If you've been doing the *Exchanges* as written, without trying to heat yourselves up, you should no longer feel like a bottomless pit of needs. You are strong enough to extinguish destructive behavior patterns for good.

Before beginning the *Activity*, talk about what you experienced following the previous *Exchange*. Are you reaching in each other's clothes? Or behaving like a hungry fish? If so, lie still in each other's arms as often as possible, until you feel the heart energy flowing. Have there been any positive changes in your lives since you began the *Exchanges*? Have you thought of any qualities you want to add to your pictures? Any time you catch yourself making yourself wrong for something, just get out the picture and add the opposite quality to it. Allow yourself to create a new self-image that reflects where you want to go. Your past is past.

Whoops! Did someone have an orgasm? If so, refer to the "FOUL WEATHER WARNING" in the introduction to the first *Phase*.

Suggested Preparation

Sounds: Rhythmic music, followed by beautiful, peaceful music in the background.

Materials: Two light, comfortable blindfolds.

Time Out: Sit facing each other and take a couple minutes to touch foreheads, synchronize your breathing, and be still. Then stand up, put on the rhythmic music and practice your hip circles again. Try holding each other's waist and moving in small circles "against" each other. In other words, both of you should circle to your right.

Watch Dog: For this *Exchange*, **she** is the Dog.

Attire: Comfortable shirts and comfortable shorts or modest underwear.

ACTIVITY

- Have you discussed birth control? Condoms have a downside. They encourage careless lovemaking once arousal levels are high. They also decrease the nourishing flow of intimacy between you, which fuels an unhealthy search for more rigorous stimulation. If awaiting AIDS test results, do what you need to do, but if that's not an issue for you, consider avoiding condoms during the next *Phase*. If he can be trusted to withdraw in time in the event of an inadvertent ejaculation, then her regular use of a spermicide may be enough protection against any sperm that find their way into his pre-ejaculate. Take some time to discuss the options with each other and reach a satisfactory solution now. Decide now who will buy or supply what's needed.

- Now (after reading the rest of this *Exchange*) gently blindfold each other and then remove your lover's clothing, except for underwear. In silence, touch each other with the goal of communicating how much you cherish your partner. Send loving, sexual energy from your heart through your hands. Feel your partner's love and warmth flowing back to you. Try keeping your blindfolds on while you snuggle. If it has not been at least 2 weeks since someone's last orgasm she should put her tee shirt back on before you remove your blindfolds, and continue to sleep in it.

THE SNUGGLE

- Kiss and snuggle each other for as long as you like with the Giving Partner taking the lead. Avoid heating each other up sexually and don't stimulate each other's genitals directly.

- If shirts are off take care not to fall back into classic foreplay. Keep all touching gentle and healing.

Exchange 14
PROGRESS

Has any uneasiness come up for either of you? Releasing a lifelong fear of intimacy is not a linear process. It's more like an upward spiral tilting to the side. You feel you're slipping backward frequently though over all progress is unmistakable. Often particularly moving experiences, such as seeing a loving vulnerability in your lover's eyes, or feeling tears of gratitude for him/her well up, will later trigger profound uneasiness. And you will be sure to assign the uneasiness to some other cause. None of us likes to believe we've been tricked (by our primitive brains) into fearing healthy intimacy.

If you rock between emotional bonding and emotional distance during the *Exchanges* stay optimistic. This is natural. Walk past your panicky feelings, and resist the urge to separate—or even judge each other. Return to each other's arms for the daily *Exchange* with as much tenderness as you can muster—regardless of what's been going on between you. Eventually you will be rewarded with a new level of trust and safety as fears gradually dissolve. Think of it as charging up a joint battery.

This is a therapeutic massage *Exchange*. If it has been at least two weeks since your last orgasm, shirts will come off, but keep your focus on giving. That is, when it's your turn to be the therapist, give your full attention to relaxing your partner's back, head and neck muscles—not to turning yourself on. And when you're being massaged relax totally. The rising energy you are cultivating is not dependent on calculated, physical stimulation. It's the natural result of proximity to a loving, willing partner.

Before beginning the *Activity*, talk about what you experienced following the previous *Exchange*. Was affection different blindfolded? How? Did you feel more? Was it fun to take off each other's clothing without vision? Be honest: are you calmer than you ever thought you would be after at least two weeks of no orgasm and lots of loving contact with the opposite sex? Does your intimate time together feel like inhaling and exhaling, that is, like arousal followed by easy relaxation? If not, you are resisting a natural flow in your lovemaking that would serve you well when it's time for intercourse. Learn to take pleasure in the energy when it flows and the quiet, restful snuggling when there's a natural exhale in your lovemaking. This way you can nourish each other for as long as you like—and enjoy every moment of it.

Whoops! Did someone have an orgasm? If so, refer to the "FOUL WEATHER WARNING" in the introduction to the first *Phase*.

Suggested Preparation

Sounds: Beautiful, peaceful music in the background.

Materials: Massage oil.

Time Out: Decide who will hold the other's head quietly for five minutes. When you finish rub your partner's chest lovingly while holding his or her head in your lap.

Watch Dog: For this *Exchange*, **he** is the Dog.

Attire: Comfortable shirts (except during massage) and comfortable shorts or modest underwear.

ACTIVITY

- The partner with the most massage experience should give the first massage. Whoever is receiving the first massage lies prone on the pad or table.

- If working on the floor, and it is feasible to do so, sit astride your lover's back. Take a few deep breaths together while the therapist allows loving energy to charge up his or her hands. Using some

195

massage oil, massage him/her in whatever way you would like to be massaged. Your lover can give you feedback with sighs and moans to let you know what is most satisfying. But don't chat. Lean forward and use the weight of your body to press harder, but avoid pressure on the spine itself. End with a massage of the head and some kisses on the neck.

- Key concepts for good technique are:

  - Slowly and strongly, *or* feathery—but not in between.
  - Stay conscious of what you are doing and how it would feel

- Switch roles—or plan to repeat this *Exchange* next time so you can switch roles.

THE SNUGGLE

When the second massage is finished spend some time kissing each other reverently, with the Giving Partner taking the lead. Now, circulate your sexual energy, as you bring your degree of arousal back to its comfortable resting state. Then be still and imagine a cocoon of loving energy around the two of you expanding from your heart.

Suggested Time: At least 15 minutes per partner for the massage.

The Stillness Phase
Return to the Garden of Eden
(7 Exchanges)

If you have completed the *Nurturing Phase* according to the recipe, your subconscious uneasiness about getting closer is slumbering peacefully. Don't let it lull you into a false sense of security. Your "Intimacy Sabotaging Device" (Chapter 5) is still there, just waiting for you to engage in conventional sex, so it can save you from ongoing intimacy. The best defense is to lay down a new, comforting subconscious pattern around the experience of intercourse itself—and then repeat it until it becomes more familiar than the dopamine-rush-from-passion habit. (See Chapter 4 on the addictiveness of conventional sex.)

Planning Ahead

The easiest way to establish a new subconscious pattern is to plan your encounters consciously. It's unfortunate but spontaneous sex is dangerous sex. It allows your primitive brain to take over. Happily, scheduled encounters offer some surprising rewards. When you plan to make love in advance there's a lovely sense of anticipation. It makes the encounter very special, like a Thanksgiving dinner.

Too often we snack whenever we're hungry where sex is concerned. This can not only make experiences more ordinary, but can also leave you hungry most of the time—because you don't know for sure when you'll be fed. When you know, with certainty, that you will have a feast of lovemaking on a set occasion, you can more calmly turn your attention to other aspects of your life in the interim.

Planning also serves as a reminder that the encounter is part of a larger effort to master another way of making love. Such a mindset tends to make you more conscientious and prevents slips. Also, deliberately designing breaks into your intercourse schedule makes the occasions when you just snuggle more satisfying, too. You're relaxed and not goal oriented. It's easy to stay in your heart and enjoy the warm companionship of your partner. You may find you truly enjoy these regular returns to the previous *Phase*, and marvel at how intercourse is not, after all, the only point of intimacy.

So how often should you make love? The answer to that question is different for each couple. Here are two guidelines:

- Skip an entire day between the days on which you make love, and
- Make love only once per day. (Feel free to have intercourse as many times as you like during a lovemaking session, but once you stop, wait until the next scheduled occasion.)

The precise schedule doesn't matter—as long as you've agreed on one. Some couples schedule their lovemaking dates around the woman's fertility cycle. Others use astrological benchmarks. This *Phase* of the *Exchanges* is designed around an "every third day" schedule, and begins with a slow approach. Try it for this week. It may help you determine your ideal schedule.

The *Stillness Phase* is quite different from the *Nurturing Phase* in one respect: these last seven *Exchanges* are intended to be done *one per day*. In fact, if you miss a day begin this *Phase* again. The more times you begin the better. Practice will help you lay down a new habit that you may wish to make life-long. Just substitute new *Activities* from the end of the book and repeat the *Snuggles*. Of course, it is ideal if you can go away together for the next 8 days.

There's a temptation to relax your intention to complete the *Exchanges* as soon as you and your partner have intercourse the first time. However, you won't see the benefits from experimenting with a scheduled approach unless you complete the full week.

Are You Ready?

Has it been at least two weeks since either of you last had a genital orgasm or dream orgasm? If not, return to the *Nurturing Phase* until the two weeks are up. Patiently allow your energy to balance, and substitute new *Activities* from the end of the book if you like. And if you've been taking a break from the *Exchanges*, with no conscious effort to snuggle each other selflessly at least once a day, you need to stabilize the flow of energy between you before proceeding. Drop back into the last *Phase* for as many days as you've skipped (up to a week), substituting new *Activities* from the end of the *Exchanges*, if you like.

Now, take a moment to discuss the following:
- What "safe sex" or birth control methods have you decided to employ if you need them?
- Have you tested for venereal disease if you need to? If not you are not ready for this *Phase*.
- Do you both feel enthusiastic about proceeding? If either of you has any hesitation, remain in the *Nurturing Phase* until you feel ready. If it has been longer than four weeks, and you don't feel ready, you may also wish to consult the *Impasse Checklist* at the end of the *Exchanges*.

The Heart Orgasm

If you are willing to move away from passion, the *Stillness Phase* will allow you to raise each other's spirits consistently. This leads to a dependable feeling of safety and joyful aliveness. It won't feed your passion addiction, but it will feed you. You will feel less hungry than you have in any past relationship, and yet you'll tend to make love more frequently than ever—over the long-term.

When the innate attraction between the sexes expresses itself through the heart it can be intensely satisfying. This is why a steady diet of sensual, deeply emotional affection is more nourishing than passion bursts. One man trying these *Exchanges* described his initial experience of this emotional depth as "a heart orgasm." If you stick to the *Exchanges* you are very likely to experience this heart orgasm for yourself. It is the only way you can wrest your peace of mind from biology's grip on your genitals. Repressing sexual desire won't work over the long haul. Channeling it through the heart will.

It is possible to experience the heart orgasm in passionate non-relationships, too—as any "Intensity Junkie" will tell you (*see* Chapter 4). Paradoxically, however, in a non-relationship, a heart orgasm will engender subsequent fear. This is because a profound emotional tie to a passionate partner triggers a separation reflex. Our subconscious tries to save us from further risky passion—no matter how heartfelt—and cracks in the relationship inevitably follow. (See Chapter 5)

To find this heart orgasm in an ongoing relationship, keep the focus on nurturing each other—that is, never make love from a hungry place. If both partners use sex only to nurture, heart defenses fade naturally, but this doesn't happen through good intentions alone. It happens because you consciously build up each other's inner strength and sense of balanced well-being. With a solid energy foundation you have no breeding ground for fear and you will choose to stay close and continue to nourish each other.

In fact, inner strength allows you to enjoy nurturing each other without feeling deprived, depleted or depressed. This is the only way you can beat the "passion/panic" flaw in your design. If, instead, you deplete each other with passionate hunger, no amount of love, sexual attraction, awareness or determination will prevent you from succumbing totally to biology. You will indulge more and more until you pull away from your partner through anger, addiction, accident or otherwise—or push your partner away with illness, clinging, jealousy or unreasonable demands. The separation may not show up for a week or two.

Remember, passion is not innocuous—simply because it leads to deprivation. It drives you to *get* or *sacrifice* instead of give. It therefore leaves you both feeling emptier, more needy, and more demanding than before. It is never satiated until it triggers a peak orgasm—because that is biology's sole objective. Indeed, passion feels so good because biology wants to ensure that you to "drive downhill without brakes." Regardless of the thrills, a part of you definitely does not like to slide into this frightening vortex. It will grow defensive despite your best intentions. You can choose the rewards of an upward spiral instead.

Each of us has an innate desire to rediscover our full potential and free ourselves from our primitive brain's programming. Heed this longing whenever your genitals propose that you'd feel more alive if you engaged in reckless, hunger-based sex. Consciously use the attraction between you to empower each other.

Practice Makes Perfect

The *Exchanges* are like athletic drills. They are somewhat artificial, but they help you develop skills you will use when you make love without them. They do not guarantee that you will stay on track—as you remain responsible for your choices. They can steer you around the most common pitfalls, though. You may also find that you like some aspects of them well enough to add them to your own repertoire permanently. One couple found that looking into each other's eyes was so moving that they began to do it regularly.

Are you and your partner beginning your relationship with the *Exchanges*? If so, they can help you launch yourselves safely into intercourse. It is common to have a lot of PEA, a stimulating hormone, flowing through your systems at the beginning of a relationship. It's thrilling, but destabilizing, and it leaves you vulnerable to biology's insidious commands. A slow, deliberate approach can help you tap the joys of closeness without succumbing.

Foul Weather Warning

If either of you has a genital orgasm during this *Phase*, put your underwear on and drop back to the *Nurturing Phase* for a couple of weeks. During those two weeks you can expect mysterious mood swings and unpalatable behavior on both your parts. You or your partner could behave as if your mainspring is broken. A craving for passion-driven sex is likely to skyrocket on the part of one, or both, of you.

The friction may be barely noticeable at first, but tends to worsen for at least two weeks. Then it will begin to fade rapidly. Meanwhile, though, one partner or the other is likely to imagine he or she cannot possibly go forward—and issue an ultimatum of departure or escape into a former addiction. If this should happen, re-read the tips at the end of Chapter 5. Realize that you have been tricked by a mindless biological separation mechanism. Resolve to stay together every night for two more weeks at least. Hold each other before going to sleep—even if you don't talk. Unless there is sex based on genital gratification, or one of you moves out, you will soon be laughing about any ultimatums—and finding the strength to drop your addictions again.

Be forewarned. Even if you believe you survived conventional sex in the past relatively unscathed you are playing on a different field now. Intercourse with an open heart is a beautiful event. The defensive shield over your heart dissolves. Under such circumstances intense closeness itself (after orgasm) can trigger your separation reflex. This occurs because you have inadvertently activated your subconscious fear of ongoing intimacy and your inner strength is temporarily insufficient to allow you to disregard its misguided alarm signals.

Also a partner's post-orgasm mood swings and distancing behaviors—though temporary—can do unimaginable damage while you're also suffering from a sense of deprivation. It requires a massive effort keep your heart open in the face of gale force emotions of anger, blame, stampeding self-indulgence, mind-boggling selfishness, unexpected emotional withdrawals (right at the time you most need to feel reassurance…) and so forth. You will long to snap shut like a turtle and not make yourself vulnerable again. (Or you will condemn your partner or yourself for your rotten behavior.) Avoid this challenge.

And should you inadvertently put yourself to the test recognize that you and your partner are just suffering from a natural hangover designed to ensure your separation and deaths. It's amazingly effective, so it's better to wait out this dangerous two-week period before moving back into the emotional depths that accompany intercourse. Otherwise you may destroy your relationship for good. Neither of you is who you seem at this time. So make no assessments of your compatibility or capacity for intimacy. Keep your eye on the lofty goal that motivated you to try the *Exchanges* in the first place. Keep pedaling.

And when separation erupts, admit it. Sometimes inner stress first appears in the form of illness or unexpected events that pull you apart rather than emotional distance. Just notice that separation is separation—and it stresses relationships.

Tips

- Monitor your state of mind day-by-day. Regardless of what an *Exchange* in the *Stillness Phase* proposes, only continue into intercourse if you are both adequately aroused from gentle kissing and touching—without deliberate, physical stimulation, sexual fantasy or sexual stimulants. His erection need not be strong, but she must be lubricating thoroughly, without benefit of saliva or artificial lubricant. If you merely go through the motions instead, you will move away from your goal. Indeed, if you force things, you will subconsciously link intimacy with feelings of uneasiness. So only make love if you sense the experience will take you deeper than ever. If either of you is not ready on some occasion, just hold each other— and begin this *Phase* again on the next occasion. Allow your genitals and heart time to reconnect at their own pace.

- This *Phase* of *Exchanges* will let you discover that fulfillment is possible without performance. True satisfaction is based on inner equilibrium, not friction. This approach may be the most serene way you've ever learned something. It's a study in not doing. The emphasis is on comfort, companionship and relaxation. It obviously bears little relation to conventional sex because it is a path to a totally different destination. You allow your lovemaking to fall into easy waves instead of trying to force your genitals to do anything.

- You're seeking to replace the ingrained habit of thrusting to a rapid conclusion. It won't yield without a sustained non-effort over a period of time. Avoid thrusting and emphasize gentle movements and periods of blissful stillness during intercourse. Though the *Exchanges* approach intercourse very slowly the ultimate target is this: **when you're adequately aroused, connect genitals and ignore the urge to escalate. When arousal fades let it go without striving to stay aroused. Connect again when you're aroused again.** It's that simple. You will feel more in the long run if you avoid deep thrusting, and when you move while connected, move slowly.

- It is perfectly normal (and actually a good sign) if your sex drive temporarily goes into a mysterious decline at some point during the *Exchanges*. This means the emotional split between your heart and genitals is rewiring itself. Relax and wait with confidence. Put your attention on making your partner feel safe and loved while you begin this *Phase* again, and your libido will return. Allow your native longing for wholeness (i.e. sexual desire) to burn through any remaining subconscious uneasiness about intimacy.

The older you are the more unnerving this temporary decline may be. Understand that it does not happen because your sex drive has decreased. It happens because your fear of ongoing intimacy has (naturally) increased with each past episode of relationship tension. As you begin to open up emotionally your subconscious passes through a period of confusion; it's not sure it wants to risk closeness again. Give your old defenses time to dissolve and your sexual desire will be stronger and saner than ever—without the stranglehold of your subconscious guardian against ongoing intimacy.

- Men, you face an added challenge. You are now the "pilot," while she is the "boat." (Chapter 9) Yet, in addition to a blind instinct to use her body to stimulate yourself, you may have a habit of turning on by using her as "eye candy." When you look at her do you feel a wave of reverence and intense gratitude? Or is your limbic brain saying, "Man, I'd like to get my hands and tongue and penis all over *that*!"? If it's the latter, you're coming from hunger, and you will unintentionally drain your partner's energy, gradually creating defensiveness. Women, too, can suffer from this primitive programming, so we also want to take care not to relegate our partners to the role of sexual stimulation devices.

- If you feel uncomfortably aroused after or during an *Exchange*, circulate your energy to regain your peace of mind. Simply close your eyes, tighten the muscles around your perineum, and "draw" the energy up your spine to the top of your head as you inhale. Then imagine storing it in your navel. A few of these deep breaths will restore your composure.

- Finally, forget everything you ever knew about sex. If you keep thinking in terms of conventional sex you will overshoot the entrance ramp to this mystery and will not find it. Treat intercourse during this *Phase* as a mutual healing rather than as a sexual encounter. It may help to review the chart on page 68 of Chapter 5, which compares conventional sex with healing sex:

If you are ready, here goes....

Exchange 15
NOT YET...

How's your state of mind? By this point in the *Exchanges*, do you:

	HE Yes	No	SHE Yes	No
1 Enjoy doing little things for your partner and making loving gifts?	☐	☐	☐	☐
2 Spontaneously feel a desire to touch and love all of your partner—especially the non-genital places you know he or she loves best?	☐	☐	☐	☐
3 Feel adored and at ease when you end a snuggle?	☐	☐	☐	☐
4 Feel increasingly comfortable with, and loving toward, your partner?	☐	☐	☐	☐
5 Keep climbing on top of your partner?	☐	☐	☐	☐
6 Tend to focus on the activities that reward you with greater genital stimulation?	☐	☐	☐	☐
7 Feel like you are just engaging in pointless activities until you can have intercourse?	☐	☐	☐	☐
8 Find yourself engaging in classic foreplay maneuvers to excite your partner?	☐	☐	☐	☐
9 Feel out of synch in bed, misreading signals, moving the wrong way—as if you spoke different languages?	☐	☐	☐	☐
10 Find erotic images of other partners or fantasy partners distract you during *Exchanges* or at other times?	☐	☐	☐	☐
11 Experience feelings of resentment toward your partner and an increasing urge to distance yourself?	☐	☐	☐	☐
12 Feel inadequately aroused to welcome genital connection?	☐	☐	☐	☐

The *Key* is located on the next page. Check it now.

KEY

If both of you answered "yes" to the first four and "no" to the last eight questions, you are ready for this Phase.

If either of you answered "no" to any of the first four, or "yes" to any of the last four, you both need to spend more time in the Nurturing Phase. *Your "Intimacy Sabotaging Device's" clammy presence is still spooking you with its defensive search for separation. It will vanish if you rededicate yourself to quiet energy exchanges at the* Nurturing Phase *level—and make adoring your partner your only priority. Be patient and give yourselves time. When you can honestly answer the first four questions "yes" and the last eight "no," you are ready for this* Phase.

What if you're in between these two extremes? If either of you answered "yes" to the first four, "no" to the last four, **but "yes" to any of the second four questions**, *you should give serious thought to remaining in the previous* Phase *for a while. You are sometimes making love* **unconsciously**, *which will block progress and can lead to regret. If you decide to proceed—and your genitals consistently welcome genital connection—do so with caution. Be very conservative. Stay strictly within the bounds of the* Stillness Phase Exchanges *and ask your partner to stop you if either of you begins to stray. Be extra loving toward your partner, especially outside the bedroom. And when you get that urge to gobble your partner, remind yourself that more than anything else you actually want your partner to feel safe in your arms so he or she can open up to you completely on every level.*

The goal of the *Exchanges* is to help you establish a perfect inner energy balance between you. Intercourse will deepen what is already happening. If you begin intercourse while you are still coming from a sense of hunger or defensiveness, sex will not satisfy. The *Exchanges* can guide you through the physical steps that promote the experience of healing. But all true progress toward reunion of the sexes is a function of opening your hearts—and progress is not linear. So, if ever you are not ready, don't have intercourse.

Before beginning the *Activity*, **talk about what you experienced following the previous** *Exchanges*. Did you fall back into standard foreplay during the massages? If so, you're off course. Return your focus to giving reverent attention to your partner instead of arousing yourself directly or indirectly. Attempts to heat your partner up set up the wrong energy flow, and your partner is dangerously likely to respond in kind. If things are heating up too much, she may keep her shirt on during the next few *Exchanges* until it's time to go to sleep.

Whoops! Did someone have an orgasm? If so, refer to the "FOUL WEATHER WARNING" in the introduction to this *Phase*.

Suggested Preparation

Sounds: Beautiful, peaceful music in the background.

Mood Setting: The man stands behind her and places his hands on her shoulders. She closes her eyes and keeps them closed. For several minutes he pilots her around the room at different speeds. Her role is to trust and relax.

Watch Dog: For this *Exchange*, **she** is the Dog.

Attire: Use your discretion from here on.

ACTIVITY

- Do this *Activity* seated. Partner A should start by massaging Partner B's hands using a bit of massage oil. First energize your own hands by rubbing them together. Then take your lover's hand and slowly work your way up each finger. Gently pull on each finger. Gently flex and then rotate the wrist. Firmly massage each bit of the surface of the palm. Use your thumb to massage the back of the hand in small circles, too. Now, give special attention to the wrist areas as you massage. End by kissing the hand you have finished.

- While your partner is massaging your hands describe your first experience of intercourse in as much detail as you wish. Is it a happy memory? What was right about it? What would have made it better? What would have made you feel safer? More loved? More loving? Then, while you do your partner's hands, listen as he or she goes through the same exercise.

THE SNUGGLE

- Kiss and snuggle as much as you like.

- When you are both adequately relaxed, or, if it is evening and you are ready to fall asleep, move into "Prayer for Union." Remove your clothing and lie together in scissors position, forming an "X" on the bed, legs intertwined. See picture, below. He is on his side, and she is on her back.

- It's fine if you aren't aroused. If you are, just enjoy it. If you're uncomfortably aroused, do the energy circulation from the introduction to this *Phase* until you return to a resting state—and be a bit less enthusiastic in future *Exchanges*.

- Merely press your genitals together, without intercourse, as you lie in scissors position. Circulate the sexual energy between you by visualizing it flowing into her genitals and out of her heart into his and down to his genitals. For at least 15 minutes, try not to change positions or move, except to get more comfortable. When you finish, fall asleep or get dressed and get on with your day. Do not heat yourselves with classic foreplay.

- If you awaken in the night uncomfortably aroused, move back into "Prayer for Union" with your lover. It will nourish you while permitting you to relax deeply.

- If ever you suffer from pain in the genitals, you are engaging in too much physical stimulation. The pain is harmless and will go away—usually within 24 hours, though it can last longer. You do not need to have an orgasm to help it pass. Wait patiently and accept that you have been given a clear signal that you need to put your emphasis on nourishing your partner rather than gobbling. Especially avoid stimulating each other's genitals directly.

Scissors position

Exchange 16
TAKING IT EASY

This *Exchange* includes intercourse—if you remember what that is. But it will be nothing like you remembered. It will be part of the "Prayer for Union."

The key for this *Exchange* is to avoid hunger. Hunger reverses the energy flow between you, and would leave you feeling empty after your encounter. So, take lots of breaks and breathe together. Unless you are in a total heart space of gratitude, lying on your partner can trigger your primitive brain to "do the biology thing," so for now, avoid lying on top of your partner when underwear is off.

Watch your thoughts to assess your state of mind. If you find yourself saying or thinking phrases like, "I just want to swallow you whole," you are draining your partner at an energetic level, and need to refocus. If you find yourself saying or thinking, "I am just so grateful to have you in my life," you're right on course.

It cannot be repeated too often that pushing yourself or your partner to have intercourse when your bodies are not signaling their obvious enthusiasm would be an error. If your genitals aren't ready, you aren't ready…no matter how ready you were yesterday. If either of you isn't ready, just begin this *Phase* again, substituting new activities. You'll be ready soon.

During this Phase, **be sure to admit it if there is an inadvertent peak orgasm**—or even the beginning of one. Otherwise you'll be completely bewildered by the subsequent disharmony or lack of enthusiasm you encounter. Experience has revealed that the aftershocks from a wet dream (common if there has been too much emphasis on physical gratification) or from a "Gee, I Might Have" orgasm produce uneasiness as surely as fallout from an orgasm that registers 8.8 on the Richter scale. So it's better to admit any possible slip, and start the first *Phase* again, than to rationalize rolling onward. If you have to back up, make each other feel good about the delay. Trust your bodies' signals as to whether or not the balance between you has stabilized.

Before beginning the *Activity*, talk about what you experienced following the previous *Exchange*. Did you make a safe pilot and a trusting boat? Did your "Prayer" feel like a sacred act? Why? Why not? Could you sense the conscious, energized flow of energy between you? Or did you just fall asleep in protest because you couldn't rub all over your partner? (Or did you rub all over your partner??) For this *Exchange* focus on those subtle energy flows. They may surprise you.

Whoops! Did someone have an orgasm? If so, refer to the "FOUL WEATHER WARNING" in the introduction to this Phase.

Suggested Preparation

Sounds: Beautiful, peaceful music.

Mood Setting: Hold hands, look at into each other's eyes, and take at least 5 minutes to remember silently all the reasons you have to be grateful to be together. Compose a prayer of gratitude for having your partner in your life. If you wish speak it out loud.

Watch Dog: For this *Exchange*, **he** is the Dog.

ACTIVITY

- When you're ready, get comfortable lying down. Take turns guiding each other into new positions using only light touch without words. Then, together, choose hand signals for the following:
  - asking your partner to stop moving immediately and inhale to relax (this can prevent mistakes, and also let you savor the stillness together when you're in a heart space).

212

- asking for your partner to hold you in a comfortable position (useful in the middle of the night when you don't feel like talking)
- telling your partner wordlessly how glad you are that he or she is in your life (always useful)

THE SNUGGLE

- Kiss and snuggle as long as the energy is flowing.

- When you decide you're both adequately relaxed, or, if it is evening and you are ready to fall asleep, move into "Prayer for Union." Unite genitals as you lie in scissors or bridge position. Don't try to kiss while in "Prayer." Visualize the sexual energy flowing between you from your genitals through your hearts. For at least 15 minutes, try not to change positions or move, except to get more comfortable (you may find you have to switch sides). Express your love with your hands by touching your partner over her heart or placing your hand over his. Relax totally.

- Connect as many times as you wish in these positions. If you are overly aroused, gently disconnect, sit up and circulate energy together. Once you fall asleep, or arise, do not have intercourse again until the *Exchanges* call for it.

Bridge position

Exchange 17
HOW DID IT GO?

	HE		SHE	
	YES	NO	YES	NO
1 Did you avoid thrusting movements?	☐	☐	☐	☐
2 Did you feel "nothing" during intercourse and just fall asleep instantly?	☐	☐	☐	☐
3 Did you find the experience surprisingly satisfying even without thrusting?	☐	☐	☐	☐
4 Did you kiss and try to heat each other up while in "Prayer?"	☐	☐	☐	☐
5 Would you be willing to avoid thrusting if it would protect the loving safety of your relationship?	☐	☐	☐	☐
6 Did he crawl on top of her during the *Exchange*, shortly after it, or at any time since (while naked)?	☐	☐	☐	☐
7 During or after the *Exchange* did you have the urge to say, "I love you" with words or touch?	☐	☐	☐	☐
8 Have erotic images of conventional sex or foreplay popped into your mind during, or since, the *Exchange*?	☐	☐	☐	☐
9 Did you feel totally safe and do you feel comfortable about continuing?	☐	☐	☐	☐
10 Did you have an orgasm in your sleep afterward?	☐	☐	☐	☐

The *Key* is on the next page. Check it now.

KEY

If you both answered "yes" to the odd-numbered questions and "no" to the even-numbered questions, all is well. If either of you answered two or more of the odd-numbered questions "no" or two or more of the even-numbered questions "yes" you're trying to go too quickly. Spend more time in the previous Phase. *When you feel stable take the* Exchange 15 *quiz again with full integrity. When you are ready to proceed pick up again with* Exchange 15 *(substitute a different* Activity *from the list at the end of the book if you like).*

Of course, if you had an orgasm, plan to spend at least two weeks in the Nurturing Phase *before picking up with* Exchange 15.

NOTE: If at any time as you go forward through the rest of the Exchanges *erotic images haunt you, consider them a warning. Drop back to the* Nurturing Phase *for a while.*

Let your lovemaking inhale and exhale. Whenever either of you reaches a natural resting place—whether or not you're having intercourse—stop. Most errors at this *Phase* are made when such natural breathing spaces are ignored.

There's enormous temptation to rush the healing process with forced performance. This is counterproductive, as it triggers uneasiness. Often the temptation is fueled by a desire to please your partner. So make it clear that your pleasure comes from time with your partner rather than his or her performance.

Before beginning the *Activity*, talk about what you experienced following the previous *Exchange*. Do you both feel peaceful today? Do you look forward to your activities together? (If not, you're going too fast and need to back up to some less intimate *Exchanges*.) What energy movements have you felt while lying still in "Prayer?" Are you and your lover generous toward each other both in an out of the bedroom? Try to do even more for your partner.

Whoops! Did someone have an orgasm? If so, refer to the "FOUL WEATHER WARNING" in the introduction to this *Phase*.

Suggested Preparation

Sounds: Rhythmic music for circles, followed by beautiful, peaceful music.

Mood Setting: One of you holds the other's head for five minutes as you did in the *Nurturing Phase* of the *Exchanges*

Watch Dog: For this *Exchange*, **she** is the Dog.

ACTIVITY

• Put on the music and do some hip circles together as you dance.

• The person whose head was held reads aloud this quotation from *Embracing the Beloved*, by Stephen and Ondrea Levine[49]:

> **In the beginning of a sexual relationship, each stays in his own body. Rubbing at the edges....It is two individuals separately having sex, together. If there evolves a meeting of the minds in the body, and the other levels of relationship are in sync with sympathetic intensity, the boundaries break and we pour into each other's space....Sometimes in lovemaking we have a sense of ourselves disappearing into the other. A sense of ecstatic oneness. Just energy unfolding within the shared spaciousness of being. No *I* or *other*. Nothing separate.**

• Now, sit facing each other and take at least 5 minutes to circulate your sexual energy up your spines, and then from your crowns down to your navels. Join hands for a moment, and look into each other's eyes.

THE SNUGGLE

- As you snuggle, experiment with different intercourse positions— *without intercourse*. Put the emphasis on comfort so you will be able to make love for long periods of time with periods of stillness. You may wish to try *yab-yum* (woman seated on man's lap), or lying on your sides, with the woman's legs wrapped around the man (and supportive pillow arrangements). Or design your own positions.

- Choose the most comfortable position you find and be still in it for at least 15 minutes. Let yourselves relax completely.

- If you are feeling a lot of sexual energy moving when you finish, lie still again in another position. Do not crawl on top of your partner or engage in any passionate kissing. And, between now and the next *Exchange*, confine your intimacy to gentle kisses and touches, without intercourse.

Exchange 18
TEMPTATION ALERT

Temptation is devious. Many of us have the discipline to do the *Exchanges* as written. But once we've finished an *Exchange* there's a temptation to go back on autopilot and allow biology to take the reins once again. This is especially true if we find ourselves snuggling in between *Exchanges*. Avoid a casual attitude. Your goal is to establish a steady state of wave-like expansion and contraction in your lovemaking. When you have finished this *Phase* you may discover you have a workable recipe for the future—one that will not lead to escalating passion. So promise each other now:

- If we want to snuggle between *Exchanges* that permit intercourse, we will only go as far as touching genitals in stillness.

- Between *Exchanges*, I will not rub around on top of my partner while naked or try to heat my partner up sexually. If I can't feel a satisfying subtle energy flow between us I will keep my underwear on so I don't seek to substitute physical gratification for heart energy.

- If we miss a day we will begin this *Phase* again. [Experience has shown that these seven *Exchanges*, together, are useful in establishing a new habit.]

If at any time you feel your partner is giving you a double message, speak up. It's all right to say, "You say you're in the mood to make love, but your body says otherwise. How about holding me awhile, and we'll see how we feel later?" Or, "you say you're feeling really satisfied with this approach, but now you're thrusting, or writhing seductively. Have you changed agendas?"

Now, take some time to get clear about your objective. Are you open to further transformation? Are you willing to feel nothing but openhearted compassion for your ex-lovers as well as anyone who ever wronged you? In fact, do you want to see everyone's total innocence despite mankind's madness? These are some of the shifts in perception that accompany this approach to lovemaking. You will grasp what is truly at stake in sexual union. Together you can help end the nasty separation virus infecting humanity.

Before beginning the *Activity*, talk about what you experienced following the previous *Exchange*. How are you doing with the motionless snuggle in which only energy moves? If you are simply falling asleep the moment you lie still, you are missing the point of this *Phase*. This time consciously get in touch with your sexual desire, direct it into your lover's heart (without moving), and visualize it coming back to you joined with his or hers. Trust that something is happening even if it's subtle. If you insist on moving or kissing during "Prayer" you are still looking outside yourself for a sense of wholeness that can only be found at a shared energy level. Have you used the signals you worked out for stopping all movement, moving into spoon position, and letting your partner know how much you adore him or her? If not, try to incorporate them in your snuggling.

Whoops! Did someone have an orgasm? If so, refer to the "FOUL WEATHER WARNING" in the introduction to this *Phase*.

Suggested Preparation

Sounds: Beautiful, peaceful music in the background.

Mood Setting: Sit in chairs, or sit in his lap, facing him on a chair, and synchronize your breathing for at least 5 minutes.

Watch Dog: For this *Exchange*, **he** is the Dog.

Attire: Modest underwear until the "Prayer for Union."

219

ACTIVITY

- Each of you slowly reads one of these quotations to the other. The first one comes from *Taoist Secrets of Love: Cultivating Male Sexual Energy*:[50]

  It is a state of prolonged orgasm....It is a fusion of opposites, a meltdown....This releases a tremendous energy that is truly thrilling as it radiates out to fill every cell of your body and joins it together with your lover.

- This one is from *Sexual Energy Ecstasy*[51]:

  The end result can be a peaceful, luminous ecstasy that even poetry does not describe.

- Take turns asking each other, "what do I do that makes you feel most loved?" If it's convenient do it now.

THE SNUGGLE

- Snuggle safely for as long as you like.

- When you are both adequately relaxed, or, if it is evening and you are ready to fall asleep, move into your favorite, comfortable position and merely press your genitals together.

- Place a hand near your lover's heart. With each in-breath, visualize your sexual energy flowing up your spine, through your hand into your lover's heart, and then down to your lover's genitals and back to yours. For at least 15 minutes, try not to change positions or move, except to get more comfortable. Then relax totally.

Exchange 19
SELF LOVE & SELFLESS LOVE

Do you sense changes in yourself since you've been doing the *Exchanges*?

I feel as if I'm awakening from a bad dream. I thought I liked myself, but I certainly didn't like the things I found myself doing. I would watch myself pull away from my partner and think, "there I go again," and yet I couldn't prevent it. Even though things are already very different I don't feel like I've changed. I feel like I'm just more who I really was. I keep my commitments, I get more done than ever before, and my relationship is going more smoothly than any other. It all feels natural and effortless—and I definitely like who I am.

Your partner's loving presence in your life is enough to allow you to function with a greater sense of well-being. You don't need your partner's money or help—though giving always benefits you both. What you really need is the balance and stability attained through mutual caring and closeness. They are the keys to the beneficial changes that accompany this other approach to lovemaking. In other words, you avoid focusing on physical gratification (with or without orgasm) to prevent biology from making you driven and self-centered—or sacrificing and exhausted. A focus on giving ensures that your relationship continues to thrive.

Most of us have been hooked on the addictiveness of orgasm for so long that we have lost sight of who we really are. As one friend put it, "basically it's as if I've been taking a drug since I started jerking off a lot at age 12." By this point in the *Exchanges*, however, the real you is probably shining through your former disguise. If so, you've discovered that giving was, indeed, the key to your newfound sense of well-being.

Before beginning the *Activity*, talk about what you experienced following the previous *Exchange*. Since beginning the *Exchanges* have you had intercourse in any position other than scissors, bridge or *yab-yum*? If so, begin this *Phase* again now—you have derailed. Do you both feel ready for intercourse? Have your genitals been aroused enough to connect? If not, begin this *Phase* again.

Whoops! Did someone have an orgasm? If so, refer to the "FOUL WEATHER WARNING" in the introduction to this *Phase*.

Suggested Preparation

Sounds: Beautiful music and beautiful, peaceful music.

Mood Setting: Tell your partner something(s) you really like about your time with him or her while you rub his or her shoulders for a couple of minutes. Switch roles.

Watch Dog: For this *Exchange*, **she** is the Dog.

ACTIVITY

• If you have a bathtub, hot tub or large shower, try bathing or soaking together before this, or a future, *Exchange*. Be sure to wash your lover, not yourself. Let him/her wash you. If you shampoo, do that for each other, too.

• Discuss what changes you've felt in yourselves, if any.

• Each of you reads one of these quotations to the other. These come from *Sacred Sexuality*.[52]

> *[After a night of lovemaking]* **I felt as though I was conscious or constantly awake on some higher plane. The entire day I remember feeling *totally* and *perfectly* relaxed. In this perfect relaxation I stood outside of time. To say there was no**

beginning or ending of time would seem irrelevant. There was simply no time....*[I was aware that everything material]* was all spontaneously and playfully arising from one great source....Somehow I had become infinity with eyes. I felt as if I had just been born in that moment, or that I had been asleep all my life and had just awakened. I also remember thinking that this was the true condition of everyone and that everyone could know this....This particular moment remains, seventeen years later, the single most significant moment of my life....I remained in this state of edgelessness for about three weeks, and life was intensely magnified....I ate almost nothing during this period....I remember telling my lover that it felt as if my spine were plugged into the "universal socket" and that it was a source of infinite energy....During this time I was more creative than I had ever been (or have been since) both at work and outside of work....I also became prescient, seeing into the future and then later experiencing the scenes I had foreseen down to the last detail....I loved everyone, including my lover, the same, infinitely. There was really no one separate to love.

All of a sudden I felt no separation between us....It was so uncomplicated and natural, and my mind was amazingly calm and quiet.

THE SNUGGLE

- The woman takes the lead, using her kisses, touches and the gentle movements of her body on top of him or next to him to make him feel loved. Limit direct genital stimulation to the most fleeting and affectionate of gestures, focusing instead on the rest of his body. Make no effort to stimulate an erection. Avoid oral sex. If he grows overly aroused, lie still next to him, synchronize breathing and gently hold his penis until he calms down.

- See his body as a three dimensional extension of his spirit. Sense him as a shining light to whom you want to communicate (1) how adored he is— and (2) how honored you feel to be nurturing him and uniting with him. Keep your touch gentle and reverent.

- This is an "intercourse *Exchange*" so, if you are both ready, you may connect genitals and lie still. Choose scissors, bridge, *yab-yum* or "woman on top" position. Have intercourse as often as you like, but keep the movements gentle and avoid deep thrusting. Pause frequently to savor the stillness and more subtle energy flows. Stop when the energy stops flowing for either of you. Don't try to heat yourselves up.

- Should you sense your partner becoming too hot, tensing up, or constricting his breathing, stop, suggest you both circulate your energy, and relax totally. You would do well to ignore your partner's sincere and convincing assurances that he has it all under control. Your intuition is more reliable under such circumstances than his assessment. Likewise, he should keep you away from The Edge, and counsel the same countermeasures.

- And, you, Sir, remember that your sole responsibility is to relax and enjoy your lover's creative touches and affectionate generosity. Stay seated, or on your back or side, as she directs. And if she directs you to lie on top of her while you are both naked, don't. She has lost sight of the goal temporarily.

- In between *Exchanges*, avoid intercourse, though you may always end your snuggling with "Prayer for Union" or some other comfortable position, without intercourse.

Exchange 20
THE BRIDGE

Inspired harmony is the ideal precondition for personal growth, creative solutions and effortless cooperation with others. By learning to use sex and your relationship to attain inner balance, you gradually quiet the forces within that formerly drove you to seek externally for a sense of satisfaction. And, with fewer power struggles and personality conflicts, you have the time, energy and resources for assisting others and fulfilling your larger goals.

After a year of making love this other way one of my friends said, "this has been the happiest period of my life." Happiness heals. It insures a body chemistry that feels good, stays balanced, and makes you more youthful. When you feel good you also tend to eat better and exercise appropriately. Moreover, happiness increases your confidence, helps you see the humor in things, and lets you focus on answers rather than problems.

Biology cares nothing for happiness. It would have you oscillate between costly indulgence and toxic isolation. Fortunately, you now know there's a middle way that lets you feel totally alive and enjoy making love frequently without setting off a sense of deprivation. Once you experience for yourself this unfamiliar—but revitalizing—path, you can more easily cope with those who are still brainwashed by biology. You can simply point to the solution to humanity's perennial sense of deprivation with compassion. You become a living example of the benefits of healing relationships.

According to various esoteric traditions around the world, this simple change in habits is not merely a path to harmony, but also a path to full spiritual awakening—a sort of bridge between human limitation and true liberation. It may be that some of us chose to come back with a lot of sexual energy just so we would discover that the world's proposed solutions for the fallout from biological sex don't work. That realization may, at first, have been unwelcome, but ultimately it has motivated us to try a better way. So see a larger purpose in your sexual encounters. You may be among the vanguard of a major healing force on the planet.

Inner balance aligns you with a larger flow of energy. That is, you sense more easily where you should be, what you should be doing for the greater good, and with whom. In this regard, you may both feel drawn to share what you've learned with new partners. As unsettling as this concept can be, nothing convinces you of the power of healing sexual relationships more effectively than sharing your ability to heal with another. At last you recognize that your remarkable harmony is, indeed, a product of your new habits, and not of the unique chemistry between you and your current partner. So if you both feel guided to share what you've learned, or if you are pulled apart by "the giant hand of fate," seize the opportunity to share your gift with another.

Before beginning the *Activity*, talk about what you experienced following the previous *Exchange*. What did you like best that she did? Did anything surprise you? Did you feel adored? Do you feel complete today? Did you allow yourselves any periods of stillness to see if you could feel the subtle energy moving? Did you stop making love when the energy stopped flowing, or try to stimulate each other back to another high? Try stopping when the energy stops. Do you feel a larger purpose in what you are doing together? Do both your bodies easily become aroused? If not, you are going too quickly. Return to the *Nurturing Phase* and wait until your bodies are enthusiastic about proceeding—without resorting to conventional foreplay. Was there any vigorous thrusting? If so, begin this *Phase* again.

Whoops! Did someone have an orgasm? If so, refer to the "FOUL WEATHER WARNING" in the introduction to this *Phase*.

Suggested Preparation

Sounds: Beautiful, peaceful music.

Materials: Blankets or a mat.

Mood Setting: Sit facing each other. Put your right hand on your lover's heart and your left hand over your partner's hand on your heart. Look into each other's eyes as you send healing energy into your partner's chest.

Watch Dog: For this *Exchange*, **he** is the Dog.

ACTIVITY

- Partner A lies on the floor on a blanket in the position he or she usually curls into when feeling abandoned, unloved or betrayed. Partner B kneels by his or her head and gently holds it for a moment, eyes closed.

- Then—with lots of kisses—Partner B and slowly takes at least 5 minutes to untangle Partner A gently, limb by limb, until he or she is resting comfortably on his or her back, palms up, arms and legs straight yet relaxed. Partner B should make a conscious effort to send Partner A healing energy to dissolve all old programming relating to defensive isolation.

- When Partner B has finished, Partner A thanks Partner B by holding him or her for a while.

- Switch roles.

THE SNUGGLE

- He should use his kisses, touches and desire-to-merge to make her feel loved—rather than hot. Relax frequently. Do not connect genitals. Just allow yourselves to calm down in between periods of arousal.

- Should you sense your partner becoming too hot, tensing up, or constricting her breathing, stop, suggest you both circulate your energy, and relax totally. She should counsel the same countermeasures if necessary. Stay focused on the flow of energy between you.

- Even though you are not having intercourse make love in waves for as long as the energy is flowing for both of you. Stop when it stops for either of you. You may find it calming to do a "Prayer for Union," or lie still in your comfortable intercourse position, but without intercourse.

NOTE: If you have a tape recorder prepare for the next *Exchange* by making a meditation tape in advance. The text for the tape appears in bold text in the next *Exchange*.

Exchange 21
THE FINISH LINE

This *Exchange* is the last one. So check your *Harmony Index*. It may help you assess whether the *Exchanges* have benefited you. Check off the statements that are true for you, though you may be firmly convinced the changes have nothing to do with the *Exchanges*. (To be sure, you can only evaluate their effects if you did the *Exchanges* as written.)

Harmony Index

Since we began the *Exchanges*,

HE SHE

☐ ☐   **I'm sleeping better.**

☐ ☐   **I've cut back on, or dropped, an unhealthy addiction.**

☐ ☐   **My health has noticeably improved in some way.**

☐ ☐   **I'm thinking more clearly.**

☐ ☐   **I'm in less pain.**

☐ ☐   **I'm smiling more.**

☐ ☐   **I'm more productive and deal with tough problems more effectively.**

☐ ☐   **The kids are behaving better.**

☐ ☐   **I'm bickering with my partner, in-laws, or bothersome bureaucrats less.**

☐ ☐   **I feel more loved.**

☐ ☐   **I'm watching TV less.**

☐ ☐   **I feel like we'll always be friends whatever happens.**

☐ ☐   **Aspects of our relationship have healed.**

☐ ☐   **I'm less broke, exhausted and rushed.**

☐ ☐   **My fear of intimacy has decreased.**

☐ ☐   **I have fewer hassles at work.**

☐ ☐   **I've lightened up.**

☐ ☐   **I feel more youthful.**

☐ ☐   **I seem to be developing more psychic ability.**

☐ ☐   **I have a sense of optimism about the future.**

Do you plan to stick with your new lovemaking habits? It can take a few months of consistent practice with this new approach to register the full benefits. If you decide to return to your old habits you may want to check this index again in a month to see how many of the statements above are true for you then.

Remember, mankind was never kicked out of paradise. We've just thoroughly ignored its presence thanks to our vibration lowering grabbing, sacrificing and isolating mentalities of the past. The costs of conventional sex have been far greater than we realized, and the rewards of changing our ways are, too.

Before beginning the *Activity*, talk about what you experienced following the previous *Exchange*. Which *Activities* or *Mood Setting* exercises did each of you like most? Want to add them to your lovemaking repertoire? How did it feel to have your lover gently untangle you from your "miserable" position? Do you think the feeling of being comforted will stay with you? Do you feel anything well up in your heart as you look into your lover's eyes for the *Mood Setting* exercise? By contrast, do you think you have reached an impasse? If so, you may find the checklist on the pages after this *Exchange* useful.

Whoops! Did someone have an orgasm? If so, refer to the "FOUL WEATHER WARNING" in the introduction to this *Phase*.

Suggested Preparation

Sounds: Beautiful, peaceful music.

Mood Setting: Discuss your ideal schedule for making love and agree on a formula for setting specific future dates now.

Watch Dog: For this *Exchange*, **she** is the Dog.

ACTIVITY

If you haven't prepared a tape in advance, take turns reading the following to each other slowly. Use your imaginations to visualize the images as vividly as possible. The listener/s should sit comfortably with back straight and stare at a candle flame or a fixed spot straight in front of his/her forehead. If possible, hold hands or touch.

Text: *[To be read calmly and slowly with love. Pause briefly at each ellipsis, and the reader should take a deep, slow breath at each " * "]*

Close your eyes and take long, slow breaths....Breathe out as slowly as possible. * Now, imagine a point at the top of your head....As you breathe out, allow your awareness to drift from this point down through your body and deep into the earth beneath you....With each exhalation it drops farther down, like a flat stone settling in fathoms of deep water.

* Now, with each inhalation, imagine you are drawing energy up from deep within the earth....It is a vibrant, wholesome, nourishing energy....It glows with the radiant green color of a healthy leaf in sunlight. * Let it flood your body with tingling energy * You draw it up from the earth, then shower it out from the top of your head and let it fall around you continuously.

* Now, imagine an infinite supply of sparkling, golden light above your head. * Imagine that a gentle ray of this light enters the top of your head with its energizing, healing power. * Begin to glow with this light. * When it has filled your body, let it spread beneath you both, like a puddle, and take the shape of an exquisite golden lotus flower. * It holds you both together in comfort and security....It heals you....It balances you....You both feel full of smiling energy. *

Now, allow the golden light and the green light to swirl together between your two hearts, and expand to envelope you both in a radiant cocoon. * You are one with your partner....Your sense of well-being is so profound that you cannot even remember what it felt like to crave something you missed. *

Now, become aware of your breathing....Allow yourself to retain a sense of your oneness, wholeness, and total vibrant good health....Smile. * And when you are ready,...open your eyes—and see the Light in each other's eyes.

THE SNUGGLE

• Snuggle gently and reverently. If you crawl on top of your partner take frequent breaks to calm yourself. Use your energy to nurture your partner and make her/him feel loved. Do not try to heat each other up.

- When you are calm, or ready to sleep, choose a comfortable position, without intercourse. Visualize sexual energy circulating between you. Then fall into a state of total relaxation.

FOR THE FUTURE

Tomorrow is an "intercourse" day. So practice all your new skills with total integrity—and an extra dose of caution. It's very easy to fall back into old habits once you leave your drills behind.

- While spoon position is great for comforting your partner or falling asleep together it is not recommended for intercourse. It can be emotionally alienating and leave too much focus on physical gratification.

- When you move during intercourse, move gently and consciously. Avoid deep thrusts, as they tend to escalate your lovemaking and allow impulse to take over.

- Consciously send your loving, sexual energy to your lover as a nourishing gift.

- Your goal will be found in stillness, because an experience of true merging can only happen in total relaxation when your consciousness expands beyond physical sensation. Enjoy!

Thanks for trying the *Exchanges*. Send an Email to feedback@reuniting.info to share your experiences in healing relationships with others.

IMPASSE CHECKLIST

If you have a sense that something isn't right fears may still be undermining your efforts. After all you began the *Exchanges* with your "Intimacy Sabotaging Device" fully operational. While the *Exchanges* are an effective way to deactivate it, you may be resisting their benefits without even realizing it.

What if you honestly suspect you've achieved all you can together? Here's a checklist to help you decide if you have reached an impasse.

HE SHE

☐ ☐ **One of you had an orgasm. Even so, you continued with the *Exchanges* instead of backing up and waiting two weeks *and* until you could honestly answer the *Exchange 15* questions necessary to move safely into intercourse.** [If you checked this box you need look no further for the cause of your disharmony. Just drop into *Nurturing Phase* again and follow directions. Don't try to assess your compatibility until you have completed the *Exchanges*.]

☐ ☐ **There is a growing feeling of uneasy tension between you that doesn't abate.**

☐ ☐ **Anger is erupting regularly.**

☐ ☐ **One of you constantly finds excuses not to do the *Exchanges*, or is totally resistant to the idea of doing them.**

☐ ☐ **One of you is demanding separation.**

☐ ☐ **One of you has returned to an old addiction and is making no effort to stop.**

☐ ☐ **You realize you're engaging in separation-producing behavior and can't help yourself.**

☐ ☐ **You're pushing your partner past the proposed physical intimacy limits of the *Exchanges*.**

☐ ☐ **The thought of increased intimacy does not appeal to you. In four weeks you have not yet felt the desire for intercourse itself, while your partner clearly does.**

☐ ☐ **You believe your partner is not being honest with himself/herself in some way. Perhaps he or she is just going through the motions without participating fully.**

If either of you checked off any of these items (without checking the first one), it could be time to call it quits as lovers for now, and chalk up another relationship crash to the effectiveness of your "Intimacy Sabotaging Device." Even if this relationship ends don't give up. Your loving nourishment of the opposite sex is needed. Try again in the future.

The items listed above point to some of the common ways we sabotage our efforts to get closer. They are merely symptoms of leftover fear. They don't indicate hopeless character flaws.

Perhaps you haven't dismantled your core belief that a partner will never meet your needs or will inevitably abandon you. If so, you may be pushing your partner past healthy limits, or whining about feeling unloved to trigger a rejection. Or you could be bullying your partner into reverting to past habits. Or perhaps you're pulling away on some level instead of nourishing your partner to the best of your ability. Perhaps you're holding back because you haven't forgiven the opposite sex completely for past unhappiness. Or maybe you imagine you'd rather be with someone else. Or perhaps you have an addiction to a substance, or to hot sex, that you'd rather not let go of just yet.

You'd be wise to try to face these barriers and release the uneasiness underlying these maneuvers with your current partner, if possible. You certainly will not avoid having to clear your discomfort by changing partners. It will show up again.

Whatever your results on the *Impasse Checklist*, take at least three days to think about your decision before abandoning the *Exchanges*. Do *Exchange 2* each night while you reflect. Resist the urges to demand your space or go into sensual overdrive. During your nightly contact silently ask for:

- signs to help you decide for the best, and
- insights to help you release your ingrained defenses against intimacy.

Also reflect on the good that has come out of your time together. Have you healed in some respect? Have you successfully passed through any crises and found your loving feelings returned a couple of weeks afterward? You can do this again. An opportunity to heal each other is precious and should not be discarded lightly just because of an uncomfortable period. Sometimes breakthroughs will surprise you just when you're sure you've stalled out.

If, after three days, either of you feels you can go no further, be content with what you've achieved together. Lovingly release each other with good will. Accept that you may have to work out your debilitating fear with another partner. It's better to face the possibility that the two of you are not destined to be lovers just now, and revert to a loving friendship, than to force yourself closer, or redesign the *Exchanges* to fit your imagined needs for more emotional distance or more physical gratification.

ADDITIONAL ACTIVITIES LIST

NURTURING
Activity: Get your partner's favorite snack and feed him/her.

POETRY
Activity: Take turns reading each other your favorite love poem out loud. Then take turns reading your partner's favorite to him or her.

HORSEPLAY
Activity: How long has it been since you've had an uncontrollable fit of the giggles? Since you allowed yourself to be tickled silly? Since you leg-wrestled, arm-wrestled, or even thumb-wrestled, your partner into submission (cheating *allowed*)? Since you had a pillow fight? Since you played hide-and-seek with each other in the dark? Since you picked your partner up and swung her around? Since you hid behind a door and said "Boo!" as your partner went through it? Since you held hands and spun each other around until you collapsed together in dizzy laughter? Or knocked your partner over backward onto the bed and "attacked" him enthusiastically? Or, if physically incapacitated, read dumb jokes to each other until you gasped with laughter?

Such activities could prove vital to restoring a spontaneous flow of loving feelings. They raise your spirits, peel off your armor, evict you from your unsuspected ruts, and release beneficial hormones into your bloodstream. You are literally heightening your awareness by carrying on this way. The next day, food tastes better, colors are brighter and music touches you more deeply. Your partner's smile takes on new radiance. His hugs satisfy more. The way she moves delights you more for no apparent reason. And new pranks come to mind....So, for this *Activity*, play together with the goal of promoting silly laughter, mock outrage, and enthusiastic revenge.

NOTE: If this *Activity* brings up uneasiness for either partner, the partner who is uneasy should take the lead and the other partner should be very gentle. Notice your feelings and talk about them.

SERVICE
Activity: Take turns asking each other, "How may I serve you?" You may respond with requests that can be carried out immediately, or at the server's discretion. If your request is for touch, only request services that would not carry you beyond the level of physical intimacy you have reached in the *Exchanges*.

POWDER MASSAGE
Activity: Light some candles, scent the room and take turns giving each other a gentle massage using bath powder rather than oil.

MEDITATION
Activity: Try a favorite meditation with your foreheads together, either sitting cross-legged or lying on your sides with your feet at opposite ends of the bed or floor.

STAR GAZING
Activity: Take a walk at night, holding hands, and stop to look at the night sky together.

PRACTICAL ACTIVITY
Activity: Choose a project that one of you has been procrastinating about and get started on it together. Put on your favorite music and take lots of kissing breaks.

SHARING

Activity: Take turns talking about the following:
- Your most "wicked" childhood prank
- Your most disastrous, or funniest, sexual experience
- Your most moving non-genital sexual experience
- Your highest expectations for intimacy between male and female

GOING BEYOND ROLES

Activity: Sit facing each other and look into each other's eyes. Decide who will go first. The other partner can close his/her eyes and relax completely with a couple deep breaths. Hold hands. Now, ask your partner "Who are you?" Let your partner answer, but without defining himself/herself by reference to any physical attributes. Acknowledge the reply with an "OK," and then sincerely ask the question again. Stop when your intuition tells you your partner has reached as deep a level of self-definition as possible. Switch roles.

Tomorrow, do some things that are not "you." Take a different path to a regular destination. Go work out, meditate or read a newspaper, or don't if you normally would. Join your partner's routine at a time you normally wouldn't. Turn off the television for a while and sit with one another, enjoying the silence.

TIME OUT

Activity: Rent a movie, make popcorn, and curl up together.

WHAT IF I HADN'T. . . ?

Activity: Get comfortable and spend at least 10 minutes imagining how the world would be if you hadn't decide to reincarnate this time around. How would your loved ones' lives have been different? When you finish, think about why you might have decided to return this time.

239

What have you really come to achieve? Talk about what occurs to you.

BATHING TOGETHER
Activity: If you are both at least two weeks beyond your last genital orgasm, have begun the *Stillness Phase*, and have a bathtub, hot tub or large shower, try bathing or soaking together. If bathing, be sure to wash your lover rather than yourself. If you shampoo, try doing that for each other, too. If something needs shaving try shaving your partner.

SPIRITUAL READING
Activity: Take turns reading each other your favorite inspirational material. Does either of you feel differently afterward? Talk about the material.

BACK SCRATCHING
Activity: Take turns giving each other a good old-fashioned back scratching, exactly to order, and for as long as the recipient desires. Don't hesitate to include head scratching as well, upon request. You may wish to end with a vigorous back rub with the flat of your hand.

SHARING VICTORIES
Activity: Make a fire and warm drinks (or some cozy equivalent). Tell each other about your finest accomplishments.

HARMONY .
Activity: Listen to vocal (even opera) duets by a man and woman or watch couples ice-skating (Olympic-style).

STRETCHING
Activity: Do yoga or other stretching together (you can each do your own thing) for at least a half hour. Take kissing breaks.

BACKING UP
Activity: Take turns giving each other a massage back-to-back, with no hands.

PASTA NITE
Activity: Feed each other spaghetti or noodles with no cutlery.

COMFORT
Activity: Cradle or hold your partner as if she/he were a daughter or son and be still.

SERENADE
Activity: Sing a love song to your partner. Ham it up. Switch roles. Try singing a duet.

NOTES

[1] Georg Feuerstein, Jeremy P. Tarcher/Perigee, 1993**

[2] Oxford University Press, 1976

[3] Keith Dowman, *Sky Dancer: The Secret Life and Songs of the Lady Yeshe Tsogyel,* Routledge and Kegan Paul, 1984

[4] Ellen and David Ramsdale, Bantam Doubleday Dell, 1993***

[5] Mantak and Manewan Chia, Healing Tao Books, 1986

[6] Mantak Chia, *Taoist Secrets of Love: Cultivating Male Sexual Energy,* Aurora Press, 1984*

[7] Donald L. Jacobs, *Joshua Bar Joseph ish Nazareth*

[8] Mantak Chia, *Taoist Secrets of Love: Cultivating Male Sexual Energy,* Aurora Press, 1984*

[9] *The Future of an Illusion; Civilization and Its Discontents; and Other Works,* trans. and ed. James and Anna Freud, *The Standard Edition of the Complete Psychological Works of Sigmund Freud,* vol. 21, The Hogarth Press and the Institute of Psychological Analysis, 1968

[10] *Sex, Literature and Censorship,* ed. Harry T. Moore, Twayne Publishers, 1953

[11] John Lee, *The Flying Boy,* Health Communications, Inc., 1989

[12] Herb Goldberg PhD. *What Men Really Want,* New American Library, 1991

[13] Ibid.

[14] Swami Satyananda Saraswati, *Kundalini Tantra,* Bihar School of Yoga, 1992

[15] Nicole Christine, *Temple of the Living Earth,* Earth Song Publications, 1995****

[16] Edgar Cayce Reading No: 3686-1, M.65, quoted in *Sex and the Spiritual Path* by Herbert B. Puryear, A.R.E. Press, 1980

[17] B.E. Beckwith, "Vasopressin Analog (DDAVP) Improves Memory in Human Males" *Peptides,* (1984) Jul-Aug; 5(4): 819-22

[18] Article quoting research scientist, Rebecca Turner, "Hormone Involved in Reproduction May Have A Role in the Maintenance of Relationships" *Psychiatry,* July 14, 1999

[19] Linda Waite, "Does Marriage Matter?" *Demography,* (1995) 32: 483-507

[20] Horwitz, et al., "Becoming Married and Mental Health: A Longitudinal Study of a Cohort of Young Adults," *Journal of Marriage and the Family,* (1997) 58: 895-907

[21] Catherine E. Ross, "Reconceptualizing Marital Status as a Continuum of Social Attachment." *Journal of Marriage and the Family,* (1995) 57: 129-140

[22] Lillard and Waite, "'Til Death Do Us Part': Marital Disruption and Mortality" *American Journal of Sociology,* (1995) 100(5) 1131-1156

[23] Daniel Goleman, *Emotional Intelligence,* Bantam Books, 1995, p.178, citing James House, et al., "Social Relationships and Health," *Science* (July 29, 1988).

[24] Ironson, G. et al, "Massage Therapy is Associated with Enhancement of the Immune System's Cytotoxic Capacity" *International Journal of Neuroscience* (1996) 84(1-4): 205-17

[25] Therapeutic effects of massage taken from *Mosby's Fundamentals of Therapeutic Massage,* 2d ed. by Sandy Fritz, Harcourt Health Sciences Company, 2000, pp.150-154

[26] Davey Smith, et al., "Sex and Death: Are they related? Findings from the Caerphilly Cohort Study." *British Medical Journal* (1997) 315 No: 7123 Vol. 315:1641-1644

[27] Palmore, E.B., "Predictors of the Longevity Difference: A 25-year Follow-up" *Gerontologist* (1982): 6:513-518

[28] Abramov, L.A., "Sexual Life and Frigidity among Women Developing Acute Myocardial Infarction," *Psychosomatic Medicine* (1976) 38: 418-425

[29] Dean Ornish, M.D., *Love & Survival,* Harper Collins, 1998

[30] Medalie, J.H.K.C., et al, "Angina Pectoris among 10,000 Men. II. Psychosocial and Other Risk Factors as Evidenced by a Multivariate Analysis of a Five Year Incidence Study" *American Journal of Medicine,* (1976) 60(6): 910-21

[31] Dean Ornish, M.D., *Love & Survival*, Harper Collins, 1998

[32] Ibid.

[33] Rollin McCraty, et al., "Science of the Heart: Research Overview and Summaries," HeartMath Research Center, Institute of HeartMath, Publication No, 01-001 (2001) Web site: http://www.heartmath.org

[34] Kovacs, Sarnyai, and Szabo, "Oxytocin and Addiction: A Review" *Psychoneuroendocrinology*, (1998) Nov; 23(8): 945-62

[35] Robert Coombs, "Marital Status and Personal Well-Being: A Literature Review," *Family Relations*, (1991) 40: 97-102

[36] Daniel Goleman, *Emotional Intelligence*, Bantam Books, 1995

[37] Mantak Chia, *Taoist Secrets of Love: Cultivating Male Sexual Energy*, Aurora Press, 1984*

[38] Kate Egan, "Love & Sex: The Vole Story" *Emory Medicine*, (Summer, 1998) quoting Insel, T.R, neruoscientist and director of the Yerkes Regional Primate Center

[39] John Gray, PhD, *Mars and Venus in the Bedroom*, Harper Collins, 1997

[40] Da Free John, *Love of the Two-Armed Form*, Dawn Horse Press, 1978

[41] Banker Book House Company, 2002

[42] Kiecolt-Glaser et al., "Marital Stress: Immunological, Endocrinological and Health Consequences" Departments of Psychiatry, Medical Microbiology and Immunology, Psychology and Medicine, Ohio State University College of Medicine

[43] Orth-Gome'r et al., "The Stockholm Female Coronary Risk Study" *Journals of the AMA* (2000) 284(23)

[44] Tucker, et al., "Marital History at Midlife as a Predictor of Longevity: Alternative Explanations to the Protective Effect of Marriage." *Health Psychology* (1996) 15:2, 94-101

[45] Barry Duncan PsyD and Joseph Rock PsyD, Health Communications, 1998

[46] Harold W. Percival, *Thinking and Destiny*, The Word Publishing Company, 1946

[47] Sandra R. Leiblum, PhD, "Sexual Problems and Dysfunction: Epidemiology, Classification, and Risk Factors" *Journal of Gender-Specific Medicine*, (1999) 2[5]:41-45

[48] Eugene T. Gendlin, *Focusing*, Bantam Books, 1982

[49] *Embracing the Beloved: Relationship As a Path of Awakening*, Anchor Books, 1996

[50] Mantak Chia, *Taoist Secrets of Love: Cultivating Male Sexual Energy*, Aurora Press, 1984*

[51] David and Ellen Ramsdale, *Sexual Energy Ecstasy*, Bantam Doubleday Dell, NY, 1993***

[52] Georg Feuerstein, Jeremy P. Tarcher/Perigee, 1993

*Excerpted from *Taoist Secrets of Love*, Mantak Chia & Michael Winn, ISBN: 9-943359-19-1, Copyright Mantak Chia, 1984. Used with permission of Aurora Press, PO Box 573, Santa Fe, NM 87504

**Excerpted from *Sacred Sexuality*, Georg Feuerstein. Used with permission of The Putnam Publishing Group, 200 Madison Avenue, NY, NY 10016

***Excerpted from *Sexual Energy Ecstasy* by Ramsdale and Dorfman. Used with permission of the authors.

****Excerpted from *Temple of the Living Earth* by Nicole Christine. Used with permission of the author.

If you would like to order copes of this book you may do so at:

www.booklocker.com

Booklocker.com, Inc.
PO Box 2399
Bangor, ME 04402-2399
Fax number:
207-262-5544

If you were intrigued by the ideas in this book
you may also wish to visit:

www.reuniting.info

Printed in the United States
5715